SPRING HARVEST
PRAISE
99

MUSIC EDITION

SPRING
HARVEST
Equipping the Church for action

Introduction

Welcome to Spring Harvest Praise 1999!

Spring Harvest is proud to present this new compilation -
a wonderful blend of original material with older songs and many
other resources to enhance worship. In this edition, you will find
new liturgy and prayers, together with some practical tools to help
leaders and participants in the use of this publication.

This year we have included many more rearranged hymns as we
want to draw attention to the wealth that former writers have
bequeathed to us. At the same time, we also feature many new
songs previously unpublished.

The Spring Harvest songbook continues to be widely used in
churches across our nation, and indeed across the world. This
edition comes with a hope that the material will be greatly used to
the glory of God.

My thanks go to all the members of the Spring Harvest New
Songs Forum and the local church worship leaders whose input
has played a important part in the selection process.

Dave Pope
on behalf of the **Spring Harvest Council of Management**

**Many of the songs in this book can be found on
Spring Harvest albums — available from your local
Christian Bookshop or direct from Spring Harvest.**

Contents

Index of Bridges

Index of Bible Verses

Index of Liturgy

Index of Prayers

Index

Song titles differing from first lines are in italics

6

Index — continued

Song titles differing from first lines are in italics

1 All Around The World

Driving

Paul Oakley

All a-round the world— there's a new day dawn - ing, there's a
Ev - 'ry where you go— you can hear this sto - ry, there's a

sound— com - ing round, there's a new song ris - ing up,—
pow - er com - ing down,— there's a glimpse of glo - ry now,—

— ah, —— it's a new— day!——
— ah, —— it's a new— day!——

1. There's a sound of praise, ——there's a sound of war, —
2. Let the lame— run, —— let the blind— see!—

This song is recorded on the Spring Harvest 1999 Praise Mix.

9

1a We Believe And Trust

We believe and trust in God the Father almighty
We believe and trust in Jesus Christ His son
We believe and trust in the Holy Spirit
We believe and trust in the Three in One

With thanks to the Northumbria Community for permission to use these words from
'A Northumbrian Office' © Northumbria Community Trust, Hetton Hall, Chatton, Alnwick,
Northumberland, NE66 5SD.

2 All I Once Held Dear
(Knowing You)

Phil 3: 7-11
Graham Kendrick

1. All I once held dear, built my life up - on, all this world re - veres and
heart's de - sire is to know you—more, to be found in you and
know the power of your ri - sen— life, and to know you in your

wars to own; all I once thought gain I have coun - ted— loss - spent and
known as yours; to pos - sess by faith what I could not— earn - all - sur
suf - fer - ings; to be - come like you in your death, my— Lord, so with

worth - less now, com - pared to this.
pass - ing gift of right - eous - ness. Know - ing you, Je - sus,
you to live and ne - ver die!

This song is recorded on the Double Album Celebrating 20 Years Of Spring Harvest.

know-ing you,   there   is   no great - er thing: you're my

all, you're the best,— you're my joy, my right-eous-ness; and I love you, Lord.—

2. Now my
3. O to love you, Lord,—   love, you, Lord.—

2a Families And Relationships

Colossians 3: 1-2

Since, then, you have been raised with Christ, set your hearts on
things above, where Christ is seated at the right hand of God.
Set your minds on things above, not on earthly things.
For you died, and your life is now hidden with Christ in God.

3 All My Days
(Beautiful Saviour)

Stuart Townend

Steadily
Capo 3 (D)

1. All my days I will sing this song of glad-ness,
2. I will trust in the cross of my Re-dee-mer,
(3) long to be where the praise is ne-ver-end-ing,

give my praise to the Foun-tain of de-lights; for
I will sing of the blood that ne-ver fails, of
yearn to dwell where the glo-ry ne-ver fades, where

in my help-less-ness you heard my cry, and
sins for-giv-en, of con-science cleansed, of
count-less wor-ship-pers will share one song, and

waves of mer-cy poured down on my life.
death de-fea-ted and life with-out end.
cries of 'wor-thy' will ho-nour the Lamb!

2.

Chorus

C(A) C/B♭(A) F/A(D) B♭(G) C(A) C/E(A)

Beau-ti-ful Sa - viour, Won-der-ful Coun - sel-

F(D) Gm(Em) Gm/F(Em) C/E(A) Dm⁷(Bm)

lor, clothed in ma-jes-ty, Lord of his-to-ry, you're the Way, the Truth, the

C(A) C/B♭(A) F/A(D) B♭(G) C(A) C/E(A)

Life. Star of the Morn - ing, glor-ious in ho - li-

F(D) Gm(Em) Gm/F(Em) C/E(A) Dm⁷(Bm)

ness, you're the Ri-sen One, hea-ven's Cham-pi-on, and you reign, you

C(A) Dm⁷(Bm) E♭2(C) F(D) **(Fine)**

reign o - ver— all! (3. I)

15

4 All My Ways

Steve James

1. All my ways,— all our hearts— the ma-ker's hand, re-
(2) Spi-rit's work,— o-be-dience won,— you will not rest till

flec-ted in each part. But bro-ken lives have
we re-flect the Son. His bro-ken life re-

shat-tered all of you— that we can see.
stores us in for-give-ness to your side.

Re-store O Lord,— your face in me.— Through
His cross-work done,— the vic-tory won.—

5 Almighty God, My Redeemer
(All Things Are Possible)

With energy

Darlene Zschech

5a Christ, The Image Of God

from Colossians 1

**We believe in Jesus Christ,
image of the invisible God, first-born of all creation,
in whom all things were made in heaven and earth;
seen and unseen;
states and powers, rulers and authorities;
all things were created through him and for him.
He is before all things, in him all things hold together.
He is the head of the church,
the beginning, and the first-born from the dead.**

**We believe in Jesus Christ,
image of the invisible God. Amen.**

Bridges — From B♭

To C
To D
To E♭
To F
To G

6 And Can it Be

Words: Charles Wesley
Music: Thomas Campbell's Bouquet
Arr. Chris Norton

1. And can it be that I should gain an interest in the Saviour's blood? Died he for me, who caused his pain; for me, who him to
2. 'Tis mystery all! - The Immortal dies, - who can explore his strange design? In vain the first-born seraph tries to sound the depths of
3. He left his Father's throne above so free, so infinite his grace - emptied himself of all but love, and bled for Adam's
4. Long my imprisoned spirit lay fast bound in sin and nature's night: thine eye diffused a quickening ray; I woke the dungeon

5. No condemnation now I dread;
   Jesus, and all in him, is mine!
   Alive in him, my living head,
   and clothed in righteousness divine,
   bold I approach the eternal throne
   and claim the crown through Christ my own;
   bold I approach the eternal throne
   and claim the crown through Christ my own.

7   As Sure As Gold Is Precious
(Revival)

Robin Mark

1. As sure as gold is pre-cious and the ho-ney____ sweet,____ so you love this ci-ty and you love these____ streets.____
(2) dream-er dream-ing in her dead-end____ job;____ ev-ery dri-ver dri-ving through the rush hour____ mob.
(3) preach-er preach-ing when the well is____ dry____ to the lost soul reach-ing for a high-er____ high.
(4) man and wo-man, ev-ery old and____ young;____ ev-ery fa-ther's daugh-ter, ev-ery mo-ther's____ son.____

This song is recorded on the Spring Harvest 1998 Live Worship Album and the 1999 Praise Mix.

8 Awake And Sing The Song

Words: William Hammond (1719-83)
Music: Charles Lockhart (1745-1815)
Arr. David Ball

Moderately

1. A - wake and sing the song of Mo - ses and the Lamb; wake ev - ery heart and ev - ery tongue to praise the Sa - viour's name.
2. Sing of his dy - ing love; sing of his ris - ing pow - er; sing how he in - ter - cedes a - bove for those whose sins he bore.
3. Sing, till we feel our hearts a - scend - ing with our tongues; sing, till the love of sin de - parts and grace in - spires our songs.
4. You pil - grims on the road to Zi - on's ci - ty, sing; re - joice in the Lamb of God, in Christ the e - ter - nal King.
5. Soon shall we hear him say, come bles - sèd chil - dren, come; soon will he call us hence a - way, and take his wan - derers home.
6. There shall each rap - tured tongue his end - less praise pro - claim, and sing in sweet - er notes the song of Mo - ses and the Lamb.

9 Be Still

David Evans
Arr. Geoff Baker

1. Be still, for the pre - sence of the Lord, the ho - ly One, is here;
2. Be still, for the glo - ry of the Lord is shin - ing all a - round;
3. Be still, for the pow - er of the Lord is mov - ing in this place:

come bow be - fore him now with re - ver - ence and fear:
he burns with ho - ly fire, with splen - dour he is crowned:
he comes to cleanse and heal, to mi - ni - ster his grace -

in him no sin is found - we stand on ho - ly ground.
how awe - some is the sight - our rad - iant king of light!
no work too hard for him. In faith re - ceive from him.

Be still, for the pre - sence of the Lord, the ho - ly One, is here.
Be still, for the glo - ry of the Lord is shin - ing all a - round.
Be still, for the pow - er of the Lord is mov - ing in this place.

10   Be Thou My Vision

Words: Tr. Mary Elizabeth Byrne (1880-1931)
& Eleanor Henrietta Hull (1860-1935)
Music: Ancient Irish melody

Quietly, building with strength

1. Be thou my vi - sion, O Lord of my
2. Be thou my wis - dom, be thou my true
3. Be thou my breast- plate, my sword for the
4. Rich - es I heed not, nor man's emp - ty
5. O high King of heav - en, when bat - tle is

heart. Nought be all else to me,
word, I ev - er with thee, and
fight, be thou my ar - mour and
praise, thou my in - he - ri - tance
done grant heav - en's joy to me,

save that thou art. Thou my best
thou with me, Lord; thou my great
be thou my might. Be my soul's
now and al - ways. Thou and thou
bright heav - en's sun. Christ of my

This song is recorded on the Spring Harvest 1998 Live Worship Album.

thought in___ the day and___ the___ night,
Fa - ther___ and I thy___ true___ son,
shel - ter,___ and thou my___ high___ tow'r,
on - ly,___ thou first in___ my___ heart,
own heart, what - ev - er___ be - fall,

wak - ing___ or sleep - ing,___ thy___ pre - sence___ my
thou in___ me dwel - ling,___ and___ I with___ thee
raise thou___ me hea - ven - wards,___ O___ pow'r of___ my
high King___ of hea - ven,___ my___ trea - sure___ thou
still be___ my vi - sion,___ thou___ ru - ler___ of

light._____
one._____
pow'r._____
art._____
all._____

11 Before The Throne Of God Above

Majestically

Music: Vikki Cook
Words: Charitie L. de Chenez (1841-92)

1. Be - fore the throne of God a - bove I have a strong, a per - fect plea: a great high priest, whose name is Love, who ev - er lives and pleads for me. My name is writ - ten on his hands, my name is hid - den in his

2. When Sa - tan tempts me to des - pair and tells me of the guilt with - in, up - ward I look, and see him there who made an end of all my sin. Be - cause the sin - less Sav - iour died, my sin - ful soul is count-ed

3. Be - hold him there! The ri - sen Lamb, my per - fect, sin - less Right-eous - ness, the great un - change - a - ble I AM, the King of glo - ry and of grace! One with my Lord I can - not die: my soul is pur - chased by his

This song is recorded on the Spring Harvest 1999 New Songs Album

heart; I know that while in heaven he stands no power can
free; for God, the just, is sa-tis-fied to look on
blood, my life is safe with Christ on high, with Christ, my

force me to de-part, no power can force me to de-part.
him and par-don me, to look on him and par-don me.
Sa-viour and my God, with Christ, my Sa-viour and my God.

11a Christ Is Risen

Christ is risen:
he is risen indeed. Alleluia!

Blessed are those who have not seen him and yet have believed:
he is our Lord and our God. Alleluia!

The Lord says to us, 'Do you love me?'
Our hearts reply, 'You know that we love you!' Alleluia!

This is the Lamb of God:
who takes away the sins of the world. Alleluia!

Jesus is the resurrection and the life:
those who believe in him shall never die. Alleluia!

Yes - Christ is risen:
he is risen indeed. Alleluia!

Patterns for Worship (Church House Publishing, 1995), *adapted by Mark Earey.* © Central Board of Finance of the Church of England 1989, 1995.

12 Behold, I Am The First
(The First And The Last)

Gently, building in the chorus

Steve James

Be - hold I am the first and the last, I am the liv-ing one, I died now I'm a - live ev - er - more!

13 Beauty For Brokenness
(God Of The Poor)

Thoughtfully

Graham Kendrick

1. Beau - ty for bro - ken - ness, hope for des - pair,
2. Shel - ter for fra - gile lives, cures for their ills,
3. Re - fuge from cru - el wars, ha - vens from fear,
4. Rest for the ra - vaged earth, o - ceans and streams
5. Light - en our dark - ness, breathe on this flame

Lord, in your suffer - ing world⸺ this is our prayer:
work for the crafts - men,⸺ trade for their skills;
cit - ies for sanc - tua - ry,⸺ free - doms to share;
plun - dered and pois - oned - our fu - ture, our dreams.
un - til your jus - tice burns⸺ bright - ly a - gain;

bread for the child - ren, jus - tice, joy, peace;
land for the dis - pos - sessed, rights for the weak,
peace to the kil - ling - fields, scorched earth to green,
Lord, end our mad - ness, care - less - ness, greed;
un - til the na - tions learn of your ways,

sun - rise to sun - set, your king - dom in -
voic - es to plead the cause of those who can't
Christ for the bit - ter - ness, his cross for the
make us con - tent with the things that we
seek your sal - va - tion and bring you their

1.3. A   D/A   A   D/A   **2.4.5.** A

crease!
pain.

speak.
need.
praise.

14 Blessing And Honour
(Ancient Of Days)

Gary Sadler & Jamie Harvill

With an island feel ♩ = 92

Verse
Bless- ing— and hon- our, glo- ry— and pow- er be un-to— the An-cient of Days;— from ev- ery na- tion, all of— cre- a- tion bow be-fore— the An- cient of Days.—

Chorus
Ev- ery tongue— in heav- en and earth— shall de-clare— your glo- ry, ev- ery knee— shall bow at your throne—

in wor- ship; you will be— ex- alt- ed, O God,— and your

king- dom— shall not pass a- way,— O An- cient of Days.—

Your

king - dom— shall reign o - ver all the earth:

sing un- to— the An - cient— of— Days. for

41

15 Breathe On Me, Breath Of God

Words: Edwin Hatch
in this version Jubilate Hymns
Music: Robert Jackson Arr. Roger Mayor

1. Breathe on me, breath of God: fill me with life a - new, that as you love, so
2. Breathe on me, breath of God, un - til my heart is pure, un - til my will is
3. Breathe on me, breath of God; ful - fil my heart's de - sire, un - til this earth - ly
4. Breathe on me, breath of God; so shall I ne - ver die, but live with you the

43

16   By Your Blood

throne, Je - sus, full of ma - jes - ty.

I will fall down at your feet,

I will wor - ship you a - lone. 3. In the

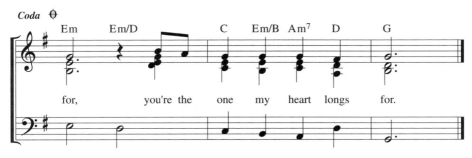

for, you're the one my heart longs for.

17 By Your Side

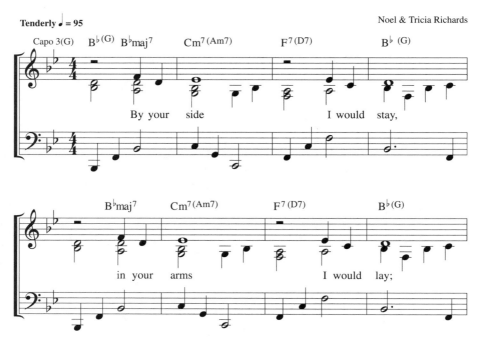

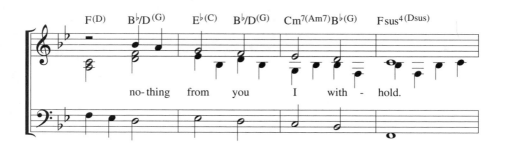

Lord, I love you and a-dore you.

What more can I say? You cause my love to grow strong-er

with ev-ery pass-ing day. day.

17a Draw Us To The Cross

Lord, draw us to your Cross which brings forgiveness:
that we may be cleansed.

Lord, draw us to your Cross which brings light:
that we may have vision.

Lord, draw us to your Cross which brings love:
that we may have compassion.

Lord, draw us to your Cross which brings life:
that we may live for you.

**Lord, draw us to yourself and to each other;
one body in heaven and on earth. Amen.**

Prayer for the people (8.47), Michael Perry (HarperCollins, 1992). © Michael Perry/Jubilate Hymns 1992.

18   Christ Triumphant

Words: Michael Saward
Music: John Barnard

Capo 3 (C)

1. Christ tri-umph-ant, ev-er reign-ing, Sa-viour, Mas-ter,
2. Word in-car-nate, truth re-veal-ing, Son of Man on
3. Suffer-ing ser-vant, scorned, ill-treat-ed, vic-tim cru-ci-
4. Priest-ly King, en-throned for ev-er high in heaven a-
5. So, our hearts and voi-ces rais-ing through the a-ges

5. Our hearts and voi-ces rais-ing through the a-ges—

King! Lord of heaven, our lives sus-tain-ing,
earth! Power and ma - jes-ty con-ceal-ing,
fied! Death is through the cross de-feat-ed,
bove! Sin and death and hell shall ne-ver
long, cease-less-ly up-on you gaz-ing,

long, up-on you gaz - ing,

this shall be— our song: yours the glo-ry and the

Gm(Em) F⁷(D7) B♭(G) B♭/A♭(G7) Gm(Em) E♭⁷(C7)

hear us as we sing:
by your hum - ble birth:
sin - ners jus - ti - fied: yours the glo - ry
sti - fle hymns of love:
this shall be our song:

crown, the high re - nown,——— the e - ter - nal name.

A♭(F) G⁷(E7) Cm(Am) Gm(Em) Fm⁷(Dm7) B♭(G) E♭(C)

and the crown, the high re-nown, the e - ter - nal name.

18a   Praise Shout
from Isaiah 12

All God's people, rejoice and shout aloud:
great is the Holy One, our Saviour! Amen.

Taken from Preparing for Worship (HarperCollins) — Copyright © Jubilate Hymns

19   Come Down In Power

Jonathan Pinnock

♩ = 110

Come down in power, let your name be known, known in all the nations; come down in power, let the mountains tremble, rend the heavens open O God.

1. No eye has seen, no ear has heard any-

one like— you,— O Lord our— God:— your awe - some might,

your strong— right hand cause us to cry to you.

2.,3.
Verse
God. 2. Our na - tion O Lord has turned from your ways, dis-
God. 3. You come to the help of those who do right, your

hon - oured your name, ne - glec - ted your praise. Lord we have grieved you,
ways are just,— your mer - cy true:— for-give us, O Lord,

turned from your face so we will cry to you.
we need your grace; we turn and cry to you.

20 Come Now Is The Time To Worship

Steadily

Brian Doerksen

This song is recorded on the Spring Harvest 1999 New Songs Album.

you are God.— One day ev-ery knee— will bow.—

Still, the great-est trea-sure re-mains— for those— who glad-

- ly choose— you now.—

20a Come Let Us Worship!

God in Christ has revealed his glory;
come let us worship.

From the rising of the sun to its setting;
the Lord's name is greatly to be praised.

Give him praise you servants of the Lord;
O praise the name of the Lord!

21 Come See A Vision

Steadily

Steve James

Verse

1.,4. Come see— a vi-sion— for all hu-man kind; whose
2. Come see— the King in— his glo-ry— ar-rayed; ma-
3. Come see— the life that re-stores and— re-makes, the

hearts were— so cold, whose eyes were— so blind;— now
jes-tic— in power, his name shall— be praised— who
hope of— the world that breaks through— the grave: for the

join-ing— the ran-somed, re-stored and— re-fined
stoops from— the heav-ens— to save those— he made,
judge of— the earth is— the Je-sus— who saves,

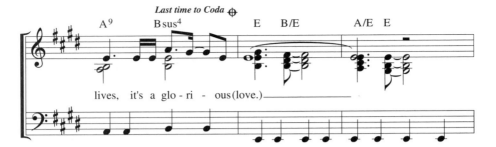

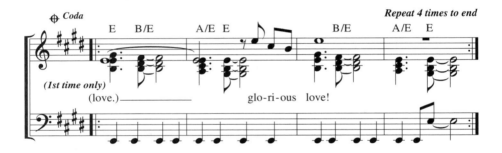

21a   Families And Relationships

Ephesians 1: 3-8

Praise be to the God and Father of our Lord Jesus Christ, who has blessed us in the heavenly realms with every spiritual blessing in Christ. For he chose us in him before the creation of the world to be holy and blameless in his sight. In love he predestined us to be adopted as his sons through Jesus Christ, in accordance with his pleasure and will - to the praise of his glorious grace, which he has freely given us in the One he loves. In him we have redemption through his blood, the forgiveness of sins, in accordance with the riches of God's grace that he lavished on us with all wisdom and understanding.

Bridges — From C

To B♭

To D

To E♭

To F

To G

22   Creation is Awaiting

1. Cre - a - tion is a - wait - ing the re - turn of the King.— The trees are poised— to clap their hands— for joy. The moun - tains stand ma - jes - tic— to sa - lute their God;— the de - sert lies— in wait— to burst in - to

2. The church— is a - wait - ing the re - turn of the King.— The peo - ple joined— to - geth - er in— his love. Re - deemed— by— his blood,— and— washed in his word. As a bride longs for— her bride - groom the church looks to

3. The world— is a - wait - ing the re - turn of the King.— The earth— is— a foot - stool for— his feet. Ev - ery knee will bow— down,— ev - ery tongue con - fess— that Je - sus Christ— is Lord— of hea - ven and

bloom.
God.
earth.

The King is com - ing,— the King is com - ing,— the King is com - ing—

to set cre - a - tion free. The King is com -
to re - ceive his bride. The King is com -
to reign in ma - jes - ty. The King is com -

to set cre - a - tion— free.
to re - ceive his— bride.
to reign in ma - jes - ty.

23 Crown Him With Many Crowns

Words: Matthew Bridges & Godfrey Thring
in this version Jubilate Hymns
Music: George Elvey Arr. Roger Mayor

With Strength ♩ = 120

1. Crown him with ma - ny crowns, the Lamb up - on his
2. Crown him the Lord of life tri - umph - ant from the
3. Crown him the Lord of love, who shows his hands and
4. Crown him the Lord of peace - his king - dom is at
5. Crown him the Lord of years, the po - ten - tate of

throne, while heaven's e - ter - nal an - them drowns all mu - sic but its
grave, who rose vic - to - rious from the— strife for those he came to
side - those wounds yet vi - si - ble a - bove in beau - ty glo - ri -
hand; from pole to pole let war - fare— cease and Christ rule ev - ery
time, cre - a - tor of the rol - ling spheres in ma - jes - ty sub -

61

24 Depth Of Mercy

Moderately

Bob Kauflin
Words Charles Wesley (1707-88)
(adpt. Bob Kauflin)

1. Depth of mer - cy, can there be mer - cy reach - ing
2. Give me grace, Lord, let me own all the wrongs that

e - ven me? God the Just, his wrath for - bears;
I have done. Let me now my sins de - plore,

me, the chief of sin - ners, spares. So ma - ny times my
look to you and sin no more. There for me the

heart has strayed from his kind and per - fect ways,
Sa - viour stands, hold - ing forth his wound - ed hands;

Bm — **E⁷/G♯** — **Em⁷** **F♯m**

mak - ing clear my des - p'rate need for his blood poured
scars which e - ver cry for me, once con - demned, but

G **A** **D** **Gmaj⁷**

out for me.
now set free.

D **Gmaj⁷**

Last time
D

24a   Christ Died For All
1 Peter 3

Let us confess our faith in Christ crucified:

**Christ died for our sins
once for all,
the just for the unjust,
to bring us to God:
he was put to death in the body,
but made alive by the Spirit;
he has gone up on high,
and is at God's right hand,
ruling over angels and the powers of heaven. Amen.**

Bible Praying, Michael Perry (HarperCollins, 1992). © Michael Perry 1992.

25   **Faithful One**

With feeling ♩ = 96

Brian Doerksen

Faith - ful One, so un- chang - ing;___ age - less One, you're my rock___ of___ peace.___ Lord of all, I de - pend on you, I call out to

when I fall down; all through the storm your

love is the an - - chor my

hope is in you a - lone.

25a Blessing From The Morning Office

May the peace of the Lord Christ go with you
Wherever He may send you.
May He guide you through the wilderness,
Protect you through the storm.
May He bring you home rejoicing
At the wonders He has shown you.
May He bring you home rejoicing
Once again into our doors.

With thanks to the Northumbria Community for permission to use these words from 'A Northumbrian Office' © Northumbria Community Trust, Hetton Hall, Chatton, Alnwick, Nothumberland, NE66 5SD.

26 Father Of Creation
(Let Your Glory Fall)

With strength

David Ruis

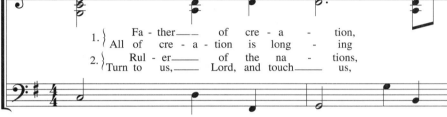

1. Fa - ther___ of cre - a - tion,
   All of cre - a - tion is long - ing
2. Rul - er___ of the na - tions,
   Turn to us,___ Lord, and touch___ us,

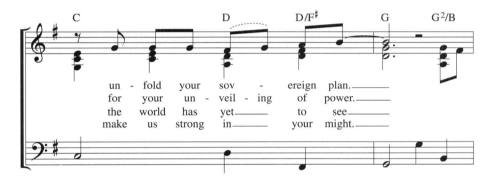

un - fold your sov - ereign plan.___
for your un - veil - ing of power.___
the world has yet___ to see___
make us strong in___ your might.___

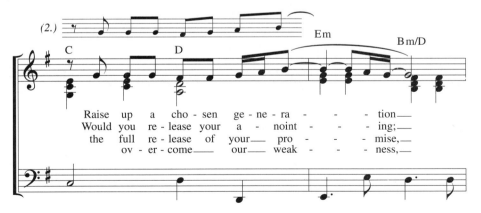

Raise up a cho - sen ge - ne - ra - - - tion___
Would you re - lease your a - noint - - - ing;___
the full re - lease of your___ pro - - - mise,___
ov - er - come___ our___ weak - - - ness,___

that will march through the land.
O God, let this be the hour.
the church in vic - to - ry.
that we could stand up and fight.

Let your glo - ry fall in this room, let it go

forth from here to the na - tions. Let your

fra - grance rest in this place, as we

ga - ther to seek your face. face.

(Men) Let your king - dom come.

(Women) Let your king - dom come.

(Men) Let your will be done.

(Women) Let your will be done.

(Men) Let us see on earth

(Women) Let us see on earth

2nd time D.%. al fine

the glo - ry of your Son.

Let your

27 Far Above All Other Loves

With strength

1. Far a-bove___ all oth-er loves,___ far be-yond___ all oth-er joys,___ hea-ven's bles-sings poured on me,___ by the Ho-ly Spi-rit's pow'r.___
2. All am-bi-tion now has gone,___ pleas-ing you___ my on-ly goal;___ mo-ti-va-ted by your grace,___ liv-ing for___ e-ter-ni-ty.___
3. Look-ing with___ the eye of faith___ for the day___ of your re-turn;___ in that day___ I want to stand___ un-a-shamed___ be-fore your throne.___

71

28 Far And Near
(Say It Loud)

From Palms 96 & 98
Graham Kendrick

1. Far and near hear the call, wor-ship him, Lord of all; fa-mi-lies of na-tions come ce-le-brate what God has done.
2. Deep and wide is the love hea-ven sent from a-bove; God's own Son for sin-ners died, rose a-gain — he is a-live.
3. At his name, let praise be-gin o-ceans roar, na-ture sings; for he comes to judge the earth in right-eous-ness and in his truth.

Say it loud, say it strong, tell the

**This song is recorded on the Spring Harvest 1997 Live Worship Album - Volume 1
and on the Double Album Celebrating 20 Years Of Spring Harvest.**

world　　　what God has　done;　　　　say it —

loud,　　　praise his — name,　　　　let the earth re -

- joice -　　　for the Lord — reigns. ———

reigns, ———　　　the Lord — reigns. ———

29   Father God

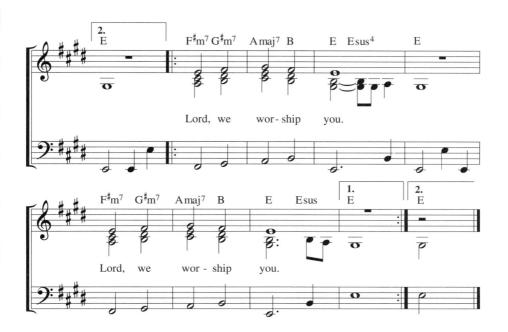

29a   May Your Kingdom Come Soon

May it come soon
to the hungry
to the weeping
to those who thirst for your justice,
to those who have waited centuries
for a truly human life.
Grant us the patience
to smooth the way
on which your Kingdom comes to us.
Grant us hope,
that we may not weary
in proclaiming and working for it,
despite so many conflicts,
threats and shortcomings.
Grant us a clear vision
that in this hour of our history
we may see the horizon
and know the way
on which your Kingdom comes to us.

From Nicaragua. Ron Ingamells, ed., *Windows into Worship* (YMCA 1989)
Matthew 5.3-12 Matthew 6.9-13 © 'Bread of Tomorrow' by Janet Morley

Father Of Life
(Let The Peace Of God Reign)

Steadily
Capo 3 (D)

Darlene Zschech

1. Fa - ther— of life,— draw me clos - er,— Lord,— my heart is set on you:— let me run the race— of time with your life en-fold - ing mine, and let the peace of God,— let it reign.—

2. O Ho - ly Spi - rit,— Lord, my com - fort; streng - then me, hold my head up high:— and I stand up - on— your truth, bring - ing glo - ry un - to you, and let the peace of God,— let it

2.

Chorus

reign._____ O Lord, I hun - ger___ for more_____ of you;___ rise up with-in___ me,___ let me know_____ your truth.___ O Ho - ly Spi - rit, sa - tu - rate my soul, and let the life of God fill me now,_____ let your heal - ing pow'r breathe

life and make— me whole, and let the peace of God,_____ let it

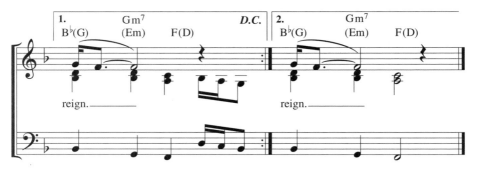

reign._____   reign._____

30a   The Beatitudes
from Matthew 5.3-12

Blessed are the poor in spirit:
   for theirs is the kingdom of heaven.
Blessed are those who mourn:
   for they shall be comforted.
Blessed are the gentle:
   for they shall inherit the earth.
Blessed are those who hunger and thirst for what is right:
   for they shall be satisfied.
Blessed are the merciful:
   for mercy shall be shown to them.
Blessed are the pure in heart:
   for they shall see God.
Blessed are the peacemakers;
   for they shall be called children of God.
Blessed are those who are persecuted in the cause of right:
   for theirs is the kingdom of heaven.
Blessed are you when others revile you and persecute you for
my sake.
   Rejoice and be glad for your reward is great in heaven.

Patterns for Worship (Church House Publishing, 1995), adapted by Mark Earey.

31 Father We Dedicate Our Lives To You *(Now Arise, God)*

From 2 Chronicles 6
David Lyle Morris

1. Fa-ther, we de-di-cate our lives to you in this
2. Fa-ther, we kneel be-fore your throne of grace, lift-ing
3. Je-sus, you a-lone know the peo-ple's hearts; we pray

co-ve-nant of love, sealed in Je-sus' blood. May your
op-en hands to heaven, thank-ful-ly we pray. We ask
all will know your name, fear and wor-ship you. We long

eyes be op-en to this tem-ple all day and night, may you
you to build a house with us, the liv-ing stones, built up-
they re-turn, sur-ren-der-ing their heart and soul, plead-ing

hear the prayers of your hum-ble ser-vants.
on the Rock, glo-ri-fy-ing Je-sus.
for your grace, seek-ing hands of mer-cy.

Hear from

32   Fire! There's A Fire!

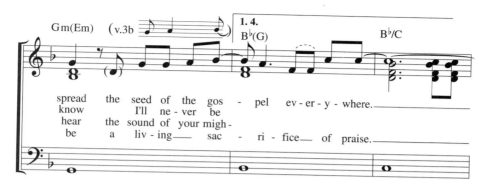

spread the seed of the gos - pel ev - er - y - where.
know I'll ne - ver be
hear the sound of your migh -
be a liv - ing sac - ri - fice of praise.

the same a-gain. For as

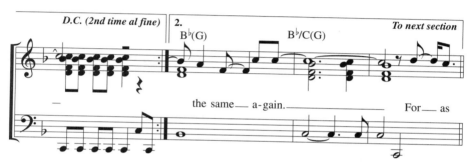

- ty rush - ing wind. Let my

long as you will give me breath my heart is so re - solved

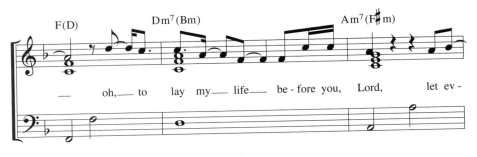

oh,— to lay my— life— be-fore you, Lord, let ev-

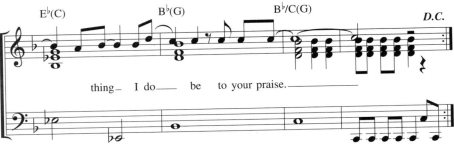

thing— I do— be to your praise.———

32a Come, Lord Jesus!

from the Book of Revelation

Let us say together in faith

Holy, holy, holy is the Lord God almighty,
who was, and is, and is to come.

We believe in God the Father,
who created all things
for by his will they were created and have their being.

We believe in God the Son,
who was slain
for with his blood, he purchased us for God,
from every tribe and language,
from every people and nation.

We believe in God the Holy Spirit
the Spirit and the Bride say, 'Come!'
Even so come, Lord Jesus! Amen.

33 From All Who Live Beneath The Skies

Music: Easter Song
Geistliche Kirchengesang
arr. David Peacock
Words: Isaac Watts

1. From all who live beneath the skies let the Creator's praise arise! O—— praise him, al-le-
2. Eternal are your mercies, Lord, eternal truth attends your word; O—— praise him, al-le-

ia, al - le - lu - - ia, al - le -

lu - - - - ia!

- ia!

33a   The Challenges We Face
Colossians 3: 22-24

Slaves, obey your earthly masters in everything; and do it, not only when their eye is on you and to win their favour, but with sincerity of heart and reverence for the Lord. Whatever you do, work at it with all your heart, as working for the Lord, not for men, since you know that you will receive an inheritance from the Lord as a reward. It is the Lord Christ you are serving.

34 Give Me A Heart Of Compassion
(Enable Your Servants)

Jim Bailey

Driving, building with each verse

1. Give me a heart of com - pas - sion,
2. I'll sing the songs of sal - va - tion,
3. We're mov - ing for - ward to - geth - er,

give me a hope for the lost, give me a pas - sion for
bold - ly I'll speak out your word; I'll let them know by my
as one voice bold - ly pro - claim; the old and the young will be

those who are bro - ken and down.
life, I will show you are Lord.
strong and we'll lift up your name.

Lord, I am rea - dy and wil - ling to serve the weak and the
I'll tell them all a - bout Je - sus, I'll tell them all a - bout
On to the streets to the peo - ple, ev - ery man, wo - man and

This song is recorded on the Spring Harvest 1998 New Songs Album.

young; help me to put in-to ac-tion the words of this
you, I'm not a-shamed of the gos-pel or what it can
child, and as we go you are with us, you've giv-en your

A **Chorus** **G**

song. And en - a - ble___ your ser-
do.
power. 3. You've en - a - bled your ser-

-vants, en - a - ble___ your ser - vants to
-vants, en - a - bled your ser - vants to

D

preach good news,___ to preach good news.___

1. **2.** **Fine**

And en -

35 Giver Of Grace
(You Are Good To Me)

Gently rhythmic

Stuart Townend

1. Giv - er of grace,___ how price - less your love___ for___ me,
2. Giv - er of hope,___ Rock of sal - va - tion,___

pur - er than sil - ver, more cost - ly than gold.___
to - wer of re - fuge, yet there in my pain.___

Giv - er of life,___ all that I'll ev - er___ need,
Now I'm se - cure,___ loved for e - ter - ni - ty,

strength for my bo - dy and food for my soul.___
show - ered with bles - sings and la - vished with grace.___ { Oh, you are

good, so good to me. Yes, you are

good, so good to me. Oh, you are

good, so good to me. Yes, you are

good, so good to me.

I've ne-ver known— a love— so per-fect in— its faith - ful-ness;—

it lifts me up to the high - est place.

A glimpse of hea-ven and— a taste of my— in-he - ri-tance,—

I know that one day I'll be——— with you.

35a Greeting Each Other
from Galatians 1

Grace and peace to you from
God our Father and the Lord Jesus Christ:
to God be glory for ever and ever! Amen.

36 God Will Make A Way

Don Moen

God will make a way where there
He will be my guide,

seems to be no way, he
close - ly to his side, with

works in ways we can - not see,
love and strength for each new day,

This song is recorded on the Spring Harvest 1998 Live Worship Album.

37 Great Is He Who's The King Of Kings

With strength

Author unknown

Great is he who's the King of kings and the Lord of lords, he is wonderful!

Al - le - lu - ia, al - le - lu - ia, al - le - lu - ia, he is won - der - ful!

Al - le - lu - ia, sal - va - tion and glory, ho - nour and pow - er, he is won - der - ful!

37a   Proclamation
from Mark 16: 15-20

Standing

Leader   We believe we have been saved.

Response   **Thankyou Father.**

Leader   Because of what He has done, we claim the authority of Jesus in our lives!

Response   **Praise You Jesus!**

Leader   With open hearts and hands we invite You Holy Spirit to come and fill us again.

Response   **Holy Spirit come.**
Silence
We need You Holy Spirit.
Work with us,
protect us,
bless us, Lord Jesus Christ.
Because You alone are our God! Amen.

Based on Mark 16 v 17 & 18, this is a specific response to this commission. Jesus said that for those who believe *signs will accompany them*. This proclamation grasps that promise and urgently prays for power from the Holy Spirit. I think it's important that leaders and congregation realise what it means to have authority from Jesus. These words are meaningless as *words*. We need to have discovered God's power personally.
© Jane Reeves, 1998

37b   The Eucharistic Prayer

The Lord is here.
His Spirit is with us.

Lift up your hearts.
We lift them to the Lord.

Let us give thanks to the Lord our God.
It is right to give him thanks and praise.

38   Great Is The Lord

Steve McEwan

And Lord, we want to lift your name on high, and Lord, we want to thank you, for the works you've done in our lives; and Lord, we trust in your un-fail-ing love, for you a-lone are God e-ter-nal through-out earth and hea-ven a-bove.

39   Great Is Your Faithfulness

Words: Thomas Chisholm (1866-1960)
Music: William Runyan (1870-1957)

1. Great is your faith-ful-ness, O God my Fa-ther,
2. Sum-mer and win-ter, and spring-time and har-vest,
3. Par-don for sin, and a peace ev-er-last-ing,

you have ful-filled all your pro-mise to me;
sun, moon and stars in their cour-ses a-bove
your liv-ing pre-sence to cheer and to guide;

you ne-ver fail and your love is un-chang-ing -
join with all na-ture in e-lo-quent wit-ness
strength for to-day and bright hope for to-mor-row -

all you have been, you for ev-er will be.
to your great faith-ful-ness, mer-cy and love.
these are the bless-ings your love will pro-vide.

Great is your faith - ful - ness, great is your faith - ful - ness,
morn - ing by morn - ing new mer - cies I see;
all I have need - ed your hand has pro - vi - ded,
great is your faith - ful - ness, Fa - ther, to me.

39a Familes And Relationships

1 Peter 2: 9

But you are a chosen people, a royal priesthood, a holy nation, a people belonging to God, that you may declare the praises of him who called you out of darkness into his wonderful light.

40 Guide Me, O My Great Redeemer

Words: Peter Williams and others
Music: John Hughes
Arr. Christopher Norton

Steadily ♩ = 102

1. Guide me, O my great Redeemer, pilgrim through this barren land:
I am weak, but you are mighty – hold me with your

2. Open now the crystal fountain where the healing waters flow;
let the fiery, cloudy pillar lead me all my

3. When I tread the verge of Jordan bid my anxious fears subside;
Death of death, and hell's Destruction, land me safe on

103

41 Have You Heard The Good News?

Have you— heard the good— news,— have you—
heard the good— news?— We can— live— in— hope—
be - cause of— what the— Lord— has— done.— Have you—

1. There is a— way— when there— seems—
2. A hope for— jus - tice

no— oth— er— way,_____ there is a— light—
and a— hope— for— peace,_____ a hope for— those—

in— the dark - ness;—
in des - pe - ra - tion:—

there is a— hope,— an e - ver - last - ing— hope,—
we have a— fu - ture if on - ly— we— be - lieve

there is a— God— who can— help—
he works in ev - ery sit - u - a -

Last time
D.S al fine

us.—— Have you—
tion.—— Have you—

105

42 He Brought Me To His Banqueting Table *(His Banner Over Me)*

Song of Songs 2:4
Kevin Prosch

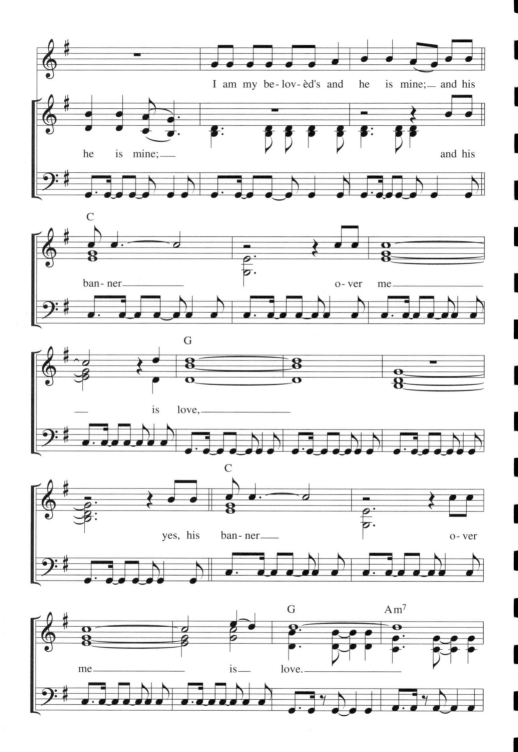

And we can feel the love— of God— in this place: we be-
-lieve your good-ness, we re-ceive your grace; we de-light our-selves— at your
ta-ble, O God,— you do all things well— just look at our lives.—

1.

MEN: He

To end

43 He Can Make The Blind
To See *(I Believe It Now)*

44 He Is Exalted

ev - er his truth shall reign; hea - ven and earth_____ re - joice in his ho - ly name._____ He is ex - alt - ed, the King is ex - alt - ed on high!_____

44a   Sharing The Peace Of Christ

Now in union with Christ Jesus
we who once were far off
have been brought near
through the shedding of Christ's blood;
for he is our peace.

The peace of the Lord be always with you.
And also with you.

All are invited to greet those near to them in the name of Christ.

Patterns for Worship (Church House Publishing, 1995). © Central Board of Finance of the Church of England 1989, 1995.

44b   The Faith Of Moses
from Hebrews 11

Faith is being sure of what we hope for:
being certain of what we do not see.

By faith Moses refused to be called a royal prince:
He preferred ill-treatment with God's people to the fleeting pleasures of sin.

He considered disgrace suffered for Christ to be great gain:
**Greater gain than all the trasures of Egypt,
for he was looking ahead to his reward.**

By faith he left Egypt, unafraid of the king's anger:
He persevered as one who saw the invisible God.

By faith he kept the passover and the sprinkling of blood:
That the destroyer of the firstborn should not touch Israel.

Yet, for all his faith, Moses did not see the fulfilment of the promise:
For God had planned a greated fulfilment in partnership with us. Thanks be to God for the gift of faith! Amen.

© Mark Earey.

44c   Leadership In The Church
Romans 12: 1-2

Therefore, I urge you, brothers, in view of God's mercy, to offer your bodies as living sacrifices, holy and pleasing to God - this is your spiritual act of worship. Do not conform any longer to the pattern of this world, but be transformed by the renewing of your mind. Then you will be able to test and approve what God's will is - his good, pleasing and perfect will.

45 He Is Our God
(Everything That Has Breath)

Steadily

Michelle Hira

He is our God,— let all cre - a - tion— bow.— The sov-ereign King,— most ho - ly One— he sa - cri - ficed his— life,— washed and cleansed— with - in, por-tioned— by faith we're des-tined to win.—

Chorus

— Ev - ery-thing— that has breath, praise the Lord,—

This song is recorded on the Spring Harvest 1999 New Songs Album.

ev - ery-thing— that's in— me praise the Lord.—

I can praise him on— the high - est mount-tain,

praise him in— the low - est val-ley, ev-ery-thing—that's in— me praise the Lord.—

ev - ery-thing— that's in me praise the

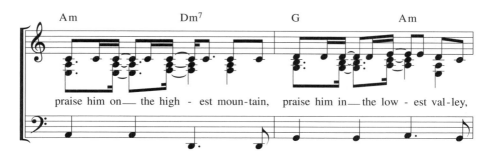

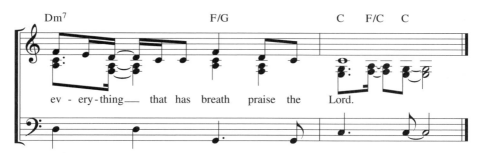

45a   God Of Compassion

Almighty and everliving God,
whose Son Jesus Christ healed the sick
and restored them to wholeness of life:
look with compassion on the anguish of the world,
and by your healing power
make whole both people and nations;
through our Lord and Saviour Jesus Christ,
who is alive and reigns with you and the Holy Spirit,
one God, now and for ever.

Alternative Service Book 1980. © Central Board of Finance of the Church of England 1980.
Church of the Province of South Africa

46 He Is The Lord
(Show Your Power)

Kevin Prosch

He is— the Lord, and he reigns— on high - he is the Lord;— — spoke in-to— the dark-ness,— cre - a - ted the— light.— he is the Lord;— who is like un - to him, nev - er end-ing— in— days? he is the Lord.— And

119

power- of God for our- sal-va-tion,— you are the Lord;—

— we ask not— for rich-es,— but look to— the cross:

you are the Lord.— And for our— in-her-i- tance

give us— the lost- you are the Lord! Send your

121

47 He Rescued Me

Country rock style

Geoff Baker

He res-cued me from the dark - est night — and brought me
in to his glo - rious light; to know his pre - sence is my —
— de - light, — al - le - lu - ia, he res-cued me. ———

1. A joy that keeps o - ver - flow-ing, ———
2. The Fa - ther's arms are a - round me, ———
3. To Je - sus Christ be the glo - ry, ———

This song is recorded on the Spring Harvest 1998 r:age Album.

a peace words can - not ex - press,
the Spi - rit's ful - ness with - in:
al - migh - ty Sa - viour and friend;

my sin and guilt are
no con - dem - na - tion
the love that bought me

washed a - way,
now I fear,
with his blood

I share his righ - teous - ness.
I rest se - cure in him.
will keep me to the end.

Coda

He res - cued lu - ia, he res - cued me,_____ al - le-

lu - ia, he res - cued me,—— al - le - lu - ia, he res - cued me.——

123

48 Hear These Praises
(Love You So Much)

Russell Fragar

Hear these prais - es from a grate - ful heart,—
Lord, I love you,— my soul sings,—

each time I think of you— the prais - es start: { love you
in your pre - sence,— car - ried on your wings:— { love you

so much,— Je - sus, love you so much.

How my

125

49 Here I Am

(I Will Always Love Your Name)

50 Here I Am Once Again
(Pour Out My Heart)

Craig Musseau

Steadily

Here I am once a-gain, I pour out my heart— for I know that you hear— ev-ery cry, you are lis-ten-ing no mat-ter what state— my heart is in.— You are faith - ful to an-swer with

This song is recorded on the Spring Harvest 1998 New Songs Album and the 1998 r:age Album.

say that I'm thank-ful,— pour out my heart,—

say that you're won-der-ful.___

Here I —

50a Christ's Obedience
Isaiah 53 & Revelation 5

Christ became obedient unto death for us:
  even death upon a cross.
He was pierced for our sins:
  bruised for no fault but our own.
His punishment has brought us peace:
  and by his wounds we are healed.
Worthy is the Lamb that was slain
  to receive power and riches, wisdom and strength,
    honour and glory and praise. Amen.

Patterns for Worship (Church House Publishing, 1995).
© Central Board of Finance of the Church of England 1989, 1995.

51 Here I Stand
(God Of Glory)

Billie Mallett

1. Here I stand be-fore you, be-fore your throne of grace, I
2. Fa-ther I come to you through the blood of Christ, I

to find help in time of need, to seek your love-ly face.
bring to you an of-fering of a con-se-cra-ted life.

seek your love-ly face. God of glo-ry, God of pow-
con-se-cra-ted life.

er,___ God of ma - jes-ty. God of glo -

- jes-ty.

God of glo -

133

52 Here Is The Risen Son

Strong and majestic

Michael Sandeman

Here is the ri-sen Son —— rid-ing out in glo-ry, ra-di-at-ing light all a-round. —— Here is the Ho-ly Spi-rit, poured out for the na - tions, —— glo-ri-fy-ing Je - sus —— the Lamb. ——

1. (Fine)

2.3.

We will stand as a peo-ple— who are up-right and ho-ly, we will wor-ship— the Lord of hosts. We will watch, we will wait on the walls of the ci-ty, we will look and see what he will say to us.—

52a   In The Name

In the mighty name of God,
In the saving name of Jesus,
In the strong name of the Spirit,
We come
We cry
We watch
We wait
We look
We long
For you.

53 Higher Than Angels

Worshipfully

Nick Coetzee
& Phil Thomson

High - er— than an - gels,—

Lord of— earth, sea and— sky.—

Seat - ed at— the right— hand— of the ma -

jes - ty— on high.— You are—

54 Holy, Holy, Holy, Lord God Almighty

Words: Reginald Heber
Music: John Bacchus Dykes

1. Ho-ly, ho-ly, ho-ly, Lord God al - migh - ty! Ear - ly in the morn - ing our song of praise shall be: ho - ly, ho - ly,
2. Ho-ly, ho-ly, ho-ly! All the saints a - dore you, cast - ing down their ro - yal crowns a - round the glas - sy sea, cher - u - bim and
3. Ho-ly, ho-ly, ho-ly! Though the dark-ness hide you, though the sin - ful hu - man eye your glo - ry may not see, you a - lone are
4. Ho-ly, ho-ly, ho-ly, Lord God al - migh - ty! All your works shall praise your name, in earth and sky and sea: ho - ly, ho - ly,

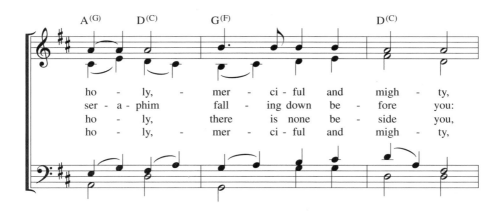

ho - ly, - mer - ci - ful and migh - ty,
ser - a - phim fall - ing down be - fore you:
ho - ly, there is none be - side you,
ho - ly, - mer - ci - ful and migh - ty,

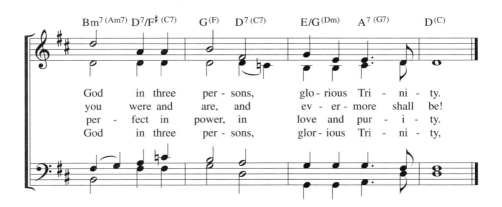

God in three per - sons, glo - rious Tri - ni - ty.
you were and are, and ev - er - more shall be!
per - fect in power, in love and pur - i - ty.
God in three per - sons, glor - ious Tri - ni - ty,

54a   Saviour Of The World

Jesus saviour of the world, come to us in your mercy:
we look to you to save and help us.
By your cross and your life laid down you set your people free:
we look to you to save and help us.
When they were ready to perish, you saved your disciples:
we look to you to come to our help.
In the greatness of your mercy loose us fom our chains:
forgive the sins of all your people.
Make yourself known as our saviour and mighty deliverer:
save and help us that we may praise you.
Come now and dwell with us Lord Christ Jesus:
hear our prayer and be with us always.
And when you come in your glory, make us to be one with you
and to share the life of your kingdom.

Henry Allon *Alternative Service Book 1980.* © Central Board of Finance of the Church of England 1980.

55 How Deep The Father's Love

Thoughtfully ♩ = 112

Stuart Townend

1. How deep the Fa - ther's love for us, how
2. Be - hold the man up - on a cross, my
3. I will not boast in an - y - thing, no

vast be - yond all mea - sure, that he should give his on - ly
sin up - on his should - ers; a - shamed, I hear my mock - ing
gifts, no power, no wis - dom; but I will boast in Je - sus

Son to make a wretch his trea - sure. How
voice call out a - mong the scoff - ers. It
Christ, his death and re - sur - rec - tion. Why

great the pain of sear - ing loss: the Fa - ther turns his face a -
was my sin that held him there un - til it was ac - com -
should I gain from his re - ward? I can - not give an ans -

This song is recorded on the Spring Harvest 1997 Live Worship Album - Volume 1.

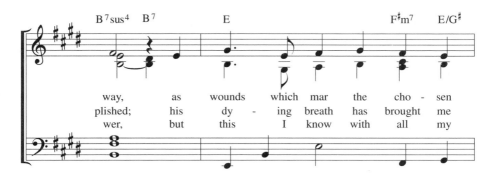

way,   as   wounds   which mar   the   cho - sen
plished;   his   dy -   ing   breath has   brought me
wer,   but   this   I   know   with   all   my

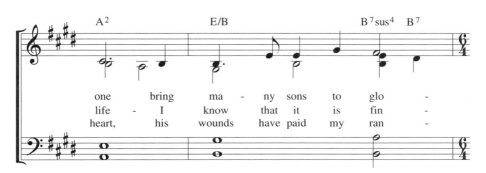

one   bring   ma -   ny   sons   to   glo -
life -   I   know   that   it   is   fin -
heart,   his   wounds   have paid my   ran -

- ry.
-ished.
-som.

55a   Great And Wonderful

from Revelation 15

Great and wonderful are your deeds, Lord God the Almighty
just and true are your ways, O King of the nations.
You have given us new life and hope
by raising Jesus from the dead.
Alleluia! Christ is risen.
He is risen indeed. Alleluia!

Mark Earey, using Alternative Service Book 1980.
© Central Board of Finance of the Church of England 1980. and traditional material

56 How Wonderful

through____ this__ land:__ we bring re - con - ci - li - a -
God____ is__ here;__ come and join__ the heaven - ly an -
prais - es fill the__ air;__ with joy_____ and with glad -

- tion,__ we bring hope_____ to ev - ery one.___ How__
- them__ ring - ing loud_____ and ring - ing clear.___
- ness__ tell the peo - ple ev - ery - where:___

56a   The Servant Is Coming

from Isaiah 52

Leader: The servant is coming whom God upholds,
the chosen one in whom God delights.

ALL: ON HIM GOD'S SPIRIT FIRMLY RESTS,
BY HIM GOD'S JUSTICE WILL BE DONE.

Leader: He will not shout or raise his voice,

ALL: HE WILL NOT FALTER OR BE CRUSHED.

Leader: In him God's holy arm is bared,

ALL: THROUGH HIM GOD'S SURE SALVATION COMES.

Leader: Then let the watchers shout for joy
and let the wasted places sing:

ALL: NOW IS THE TIME FOR DELIVERANCE!
NOW EARTH'S REDEEMER HAS COME!

57   Humble Yourselves

Gently

Dave Bilbrough

Capo 3 (Em)

This song is recorded on the Spring Harvest 1998 Live Worship Album.

58   Humbly In Your Sight

Words and Music Tom Colvin
arr. David Ball

Easy movement ♩ = 96
Capo 3 (D)

1. Hum - bly in your sight we come to - geth - er, Lord:
2. These our hearts are yours, we give them to you, Lord:
3. These our ears are yours, we give them to you, Lord:
4. These our eyes are yours, we give them to you, Lord:
5. There our hands are yours, we give them to you, Lord:
6. These our tongues are yours, we give them to you, Lord:
7. These our feet are yours, we give them to you, Lord:
8. Our whole selves are yours, we give them to you, Lord:

grant us now the bles - sing of your pre - sence here.
pu - ri - fy our love to make it like your own.
o - pen them to hear the gos - pel straight from you.
may we al - ways see this world as with your sight.
give them strength and skill to work and build for you.
may we speak your heal - ing words of light and truth.
may we al - ways walk the path of light with you.
take us now and keep us safe for ev - er - more.

58a   Honouring God's Image

Isaiah 46: 9

Remember the former things, those of long ago;
I am God, and there is no other;
I am God, and there is none like me.

59 I Have Heard
(I Won't Let Go)

Steadily, with rhythm

Stuart Townend

This song is recorded on the Spring Harvest 1999 Praise Mix.

Copyright © 1997 Kingsway's Thankyou Music
P.O. Box 75, Eastbourne, East Sussex, BN23 6NW, UK. Used by permission.

I need Your pow - er, Lord!
O let Your glo - ry fall!
pour out your mer - cy, Lord!
we need your pow - er, Lord!
I need your pow - er, Lord!

I won't let go, I won't let go un - til You bless me. I won't take no for an an - swer; Je - sus, I won't let go!

Last time to Coda

D.C.

150

Mid 8

I'm not un-grate—ful for— the bless - ings You— have gi-ven,—

but I can see— the need— a - round— me;—

I'm not a-shamed— to say— I need— all that— You have,— so

Fa-ther, hear— me knock - ing, see me hold-ing out— my hands to

You. 3. For a hun - ger that— will o -

D.S. al Coda **Coda**

151

60   I Am Yours
(Pure Like You)

David Gate

Gently

Verse

1. I am Yours and You are mine, friend to me for all of time.
2. I'm not afraid of earthly things, for I am safe with you my King.

Chorus

And all I have now I give to You;

and all I want— now— is to— be— pure,—

pure like You.

60a   A Call To Communion

Are we ready?

Where is my guest room, where I may eat with you?
Lord, prepare my heart to meet with You.
Silence
The meal is ready, where may I eat with you?
Lord, open my eyes to see You.
Silence
The time is now, where may I eat with you?
Lord, here I am.
Silence
The price is paid, where may I eat with you?
Lord Jesus Christ, thankyou.

'Where is my guest room, where I may eat the Passover with my friends?' This is the question Jesus asks in Mark 14 v 14. He was looking for the place and time where he could finally meet with the disciples and share the Passover...could He be asking the same thing of us. We know He is always ready and waiting, it is up to us to be there.

61 I Believe In Angels

Steadily

Stuart Bell, Johnny Markin
& Paul Cruickshank

1. I be-lieve in an-gels,__ God's mes-sen-gers__ of fire. I be-lieve in pro-phets, who with God's word in-spire. I be-lieve in mi-ra-cles__ and that the strong-holds fall,__ and
2. I be-lieve in wor-ship__ that touch-es hea-vens throne. I be-lieve His Spi-rit re-news the faith-ful one. I be-lieve the word of God,__ his truth re-vealed to all.__ Yes,
3. I be-lieve re-vi-val__ will touch the earth a-gain. I be-lieve His king-dom will rule with-out an end. I be-lieve that u-ni-ty__ will see his bles-sing fall,__ for

This song is recorded on the Spring Harvest 1999 Praise Mix.

call. It's the name at which we fall: it's the high-est name of all.

61a Preparing For Christ's Return

A: Come, Lord, with triumph;
B: But may we not be ashamed.
All: Amen. Come, Lord Jesus.

A: Come, Lord, with glory;
B: But may we not be found living in the darkness.
All: Amen. Come, Lord Jesus.

A: Come, Lord, with judgement;
B: But may we find your forgiveness.
All: Amen. Come, Lord Jesus

A: Come, Lord, as King.
B: And let us live with you for ever.
All: Amen. Come, Lord Jesus.

The congregation may split into 'A' and 'B', or 'A' and 'B' may be taken by the leader, and the congregation respond with 'All'.

© Scripture Union, adapted by Mark Earey.

62 I Don't Know Why
(All I Know)

Noel & Tricia Richards
& Wayne Drain

With feeling

Verse

1. I don't know why, I can't see how
2. It's way be - yond what I can see,

Your pre-cious blood could cleanse me
how an - y - one could die for

now; when all this time
me. So un - de - served,

I've lived a lie, with no ex - cuse,
this pre-cious grace; you've won my heart,

63   I Know It

Moderately

Darlene Zschech

I know it,___ I know it,___ his blood has set me free, I've been de-liv-ered,___ for-giv-en,___ fear has got no hold on me.___ I'm set a-part, not

161

know it to-day.— There is pow-er in the name of Je - sus,—

ful - ness— of joy,— I've found in Je - sus,—

strength in the name of Je - sus:— I

know it, I know it, oh, I've got to tell you that I free.

163

64   I See The Lord

From Isaiah 6
Chris Falson

I see the Lord seated on the throne — ex-
alt-ed; — and the train of his robe — fills the tem-ple — with
glo - ry: the whole earth — is — fill -
ed, the whole earth — is — filled, — the

65   I Want To Be Holy

Strongly

Paul Oakley
& Alan Rose

I want to be ho-ly, I want to be right-eous, I want to live my life the way— you want— me to.— I want to be blame-less, not walk-ing in dark-ness, I want to be a liv-ing sac-ri-fice— to

you. I'm gon-na run the race,— I'm gon-na run to win,—

throw off ev - ery - thing— that hin - ders me,— yeah,

Last time to Coda

yeah.— I'm gon-na fix my eyes up - on— the King,— and

leave my sin be - hind.—

1. **D.C.** **2.**

I want to be so much bet - ter, I want to be more like you. Keep tak-ing me fur - ther and deep-er, I want to right the wrong, I want to live this song, now I'm pres - sing on, I'm gon-na leave my sin be-hind.

D.C.

⊕ *Coda*

leave my sin be-hind.— Sing-ing, "good-bye rage, good - bye hate,—

good - bye an-ger, good - bye ma - lice, good-bye bit-ter-ness—and slan - der,

Repeat as required to end

good - bye fear of man!"— Sing-ing,

65a   God Be In My Head

God be in my head,
and in my understanding;
God be in my eyes,
and in my looking;
God be in my mouth,
and in my speaking;
God be in my heart,
and in my thinking;
God be at my end,
and at my departing.

Sarum Book of Hours (1514)
© 'The Open Gate' by David Adam

169

66 I Will Bow Down
(Living Sacrifice)

Gently

Dave Wellington

I will bow down, hum-ble my-self
Then shall I sing, stretch out my hands

be-fore the Lord_____ of glo-ry
and wor-ship

God_____ al-migh-ty. This is my plea,—

— my heart's de-sire; I give— my life—

67 I Will Dance
(Undignified)

2 Samuel 6:22
Matt Redman

♩ = 112

I will dance, I will sing, to be mad for my King; no-thing, Lord is hin-der-ing the pas-sion in my soul. pas-sion in my soul. And I'll be-come even more un-dig-ni-fied than this; some would say it's fool-ish-ness, but I'll be-come

68 I Will Follow You
(*Lay Myself Down*)

Sue Rinaldi
& Caroline Bonnett

With feeling ♩ = 70

I will fol-low you to the cross— and lay my-self down,—

lay my-self down.— I will fol-low you to the cross— and

lay my-self down,— lay my-self down.—
1. Rid me— of— these— dir-
2. Kiss me— with— your— heal-

- ty—clothes,— cleanse me— from all— this pol-lu-tion.——— I choose—
- ing— touch,— take me— to the— heat of your— fire,——— bathe me—

This song is recorded on the Spring Harvest 1998 Praise Mix.

69   I Will Never Be The Same

Paul Oakley
& Kevin Jamieson

Meditatively

I will ne-ver be— the same,—
now that I— have seen— the cross;—
and how you took up-on— your-self—
the ful-ness of— the wrath— of God.—
And I may ne-ver un - der-stand——

70   I Will Offer Up My Life

Matt Redman

1. I will of-fer up my life in spi-rit and truth,___ pour-ing out the oil of love as my wor-ship to you.___ In sur-ren-der I must
2. You de-serve my ev-ery breath for you've paid the great cost - giv-ing up your life to death, ev-en death on a cross.___ You took all my shame a-

give my ev - ery part;___ Lord, re - ceive the sac - ri -
\- way, there de - feat - ed my sin,___ o - pened up the gates of

\- fice of a bro - ken heart.___ Je- sus, what can I give,___
heaven and have bec- koned me in.

___ what can I bring___ to so faith - ful a friend,___

___ to so lov - ing a king?___ Sav - iour, what can be said,___

___ what can be sung___ as a praise of your name___

for the things you have done?___ Oh, my words could not tell,___ ___ not ev - en in part,___ of the debt of love that is owed___ ___ by this thank - ful heart.___ What___ can I give, what___ can I bring, what___ ___ can I sing as an of - fer - ing, Lord?___ What___

Repeat as required

181

71   I Will Worship

David Ruis

all my— wor - ship, I will give— you all my— praise;—
— you a- lone— I long to— wor - ship, you a- lone— are
wor - thy— of— my— praise.—

71a   Open Our Lips

from Colossians 3.16-17

O Lord, open our lips **and we shall proclaim your praise.**

Sing psalms, hymns and sacred songs
let us sing to God with thanksgiving in our hearts.

Let everything you do or say be done in the name of the Lord Jesus,
giving thanks to God through Jesus Christ.

72 In My Life Proclaim Your Glory *(Lord Of All Mercy)*

Steadily

Geoff Bullock

1. In my life— pro-claim— your glo - ry,
   In my words— pro-claim— your mer - cy,
2. In my soul— un - veil— your love,— Lord,
   Lord of all,— en - throned— in glo - ry,

in my heart— re - veal— your ma - jes - ty;
in my life— re - veal— your pow - - - er;
deep with - in— my heart— re - new - ing me.
grace and mer - cy, truth— and right - eous-ness,

then my soul— shall speak the won-ders of— your grace,— and this
then my soul— shall be a mir - ror of— your love,— and this
Day by day— your life trans - form-ing all— I am,— as this
ev - ery knee— shall bow be - fore this Christ, our Lord,— as—

heart of mine— shall sing your praise.
heart of mine— shall sing your praise.—
heart of mine— re - flects your praise.—
all cre - a - tion sings your praise.—

I give you the hon - our, I give you the praise,—
and pro - claim your glo - ri - ous power.
power, and pro - claim your glo - ri - ous power.

72a Looking For His Coming

God our desire,
whose coming we look for,
but whose arrival is unexpected;
here in the darkness
make us urgent to greet you,
and open yourself to our longing
that we may be known by you
through Jesus Christ. Amen.

All Desires Known, Janet Morley (Movement for the Ordiantion of Women, 1988). © Janet Morley 1988

73 Is It True Today
(History Maker)

Martin Smith

Is it true—— to-day that when peo-
—— to-day that when peo-

- ple pray cloud-less skies—— will break
- ple pray we'll see dead—— men rise

kings and queens—— will shake? Yes, it's true
and the blind—— set free? Yes, it's true—

— and I be-lieve—— it,—
— and I be-lieve—— it,—

This song is recorded on the Spring Harvest 1998 Praise Mix.

I'm liv - ing___ for you.___
I'm liv - ing___ for you.___

2. Well, it's true___

I'm___ going to be   a his - to - ry - ma - ker___ in this   land.___

I'm___ going to be   a spea - ker of

truth to___ all man - kind.___   I'm___ going to stand,

189

74   It Is To You

Steadily

Duke Kerr

It is to you____ I give____ the glo - ry, it is to you__

__ I give____ the praise,____ be - cause you have done__

__ so__ much for__ me, I will mag - ni - fy__ your name.__

__ It is to you,____ Ho - ly Fa - ther,

This song is recorded on the Spring Harvest 1999 New Songs Album.

no one else___ but you,___ and I will praise your___
name, praise your name, and I will praise your___
name for ev - er - more.___

74a   Families And Relationships

Ephesians 4: 1-6

As a prisoner for the Lord, then, I urge you to live a life worthy of the calling you have received. Be completely humble and gentle; be patient, bearing with one another in love. Make every effort to keep the unity of the Spirit through the bond of peace. There is one body and one spirit - just as you were called to one hope when you were called - one Lord, one faith, one baptism; one God and Father of all, who is over all and through all and in all.

75 It's Rising Up

Matt Redman
& Martin Smith

♩ = 111

It's ris-ing— up— from coast to— coast,— from north to— south,— and east to— west;— the cry of— hearts— that love your— name,— which with one— voice— we will pro-claim.—

The for-mer— things— have ta-ken place:— can

ho - ly   is____ the____ Lord!'

2. And   we have__ heard__   the

Li - on's__   roar__   that   speaks of__ heav - en's__ love__

__ and__ power:__   is   this the__ time,__   is   this the__ call__   that

76 Jesus, All For Jesus

Steadily

Jennifer Atkinson
& Robin Mark

1. Je - sus, all for Je - sus;
2. All of my am - bi - tions hopes and plans

all I am and have and ev - er hope to
I sur - ren - der these in to your

be.
hands.

hands. For it's on - ly in

This song is recorded on the Spring Harvest 1999 New Songs Album.

your will— that I am free.——— For it's

on - ly in——— your will— that— I am free.

76a   In Life, In Death

Leader: In life, in death,
        in life beyond death,
ALL: JESUS CHRIST IS LORD.

Leader: Over powers and principalities,
        over all who determine, control,
        govern or finance the affairs of humankind,
ALL: JESUS CHRIST IS LORD.

Leader: Of the poor, of the broken,
        of the sinned against and the sinner,
ALL: JESUS CHRIST IS LORD.

Leader: Above the Church,
        beyond our most excellent theologies
        and in the quiet corners of our hearts,
ALL: JESUS CHRIST IS LORD.

Leader: Thanks be to God.
ALL: AMEN.

77 Jesus Christ
(Once Again)

Matt Redman

Verse 1:
1. Je - sus Christ, I think up-on your sa-cri-fice:
you be-came no - thing, poured out to death.
Ma - ny times I've won-dered at your gift of life, and
I'm in that place once a - gain,

Verse 2:
2. Now you are ex - alt-ed to the high-est place -
King of the heav - ens where one day I'll bow,
but for now, I mar - vel at this sav - ing grace, and
I'm full of praise once a - gain,

This song is recorded on the Spring Harvest 1997 New Songs Album, the 1997 Live Worship Album - Volume 1
and on the Double Album Celebrating 20 Years Of Spring Harvest

78 Jesus, Forgive Me

With energy

Martin Lore

I lift my head,— lift my heart,— lift my soul— to— You. I give my life,— give my-self,— give it all— to— You.

78a   Freedom And Forgiveness

God of terror and joy,
you arise to shake the earth.
Open our graves
and give us back the past;
so that all that has been buried
may be freed and forgiven
and our lives may return to you
through the risen Christ. Amen.

All Desires Known, Janet Morley (Movement for the Ordination of Women, 1988). © Janet Morley 1988

79 Jesus Is The Name We Honour
(We Will Glorify)

Brightly ♩ = 140   Phil Lawson-Johnston

1. Je - sus is the name— we ho - nour,—
2. Je - sus is the name— we wor - ship;—
3. Je - sus is the Fa - ther's splen - dour,—

Je - sus is the name we praise.—
Je - sus is the name we trust.—
Je - sus is the Fa - ther's joy.—

Ma - jes - tic name a - bove— all
He is the King a - bove— all
He will re - turn to reign— in

oth - er names;— the high - est heaven— and earth pro - claim— that
oth - er kings;— let all cre - a - tion stand and sing— that
ma - je - sty,— and ev - ery eye— at last will see— that

80 Jesus, Jesus, Healer, Saviour

David Fellingham

80a Keep Your People, Lord

Keep your people, Lord, in the arms of your embrace;
shelter them under your wings.
Be their light in darkness,
be their hope in distress,
be their calm in anxiety.
Be strength in their weakness,
be their comfort in pain,
be their song in the night.

81 Jesus, Jesus, Holy And Anointed One

With feeling ♩ = 70

John Barnett

Je - sus, Je - sus,

ho - ly and an - oin - ted One,___ Je - sus.
ri - sen and ex - alt - ed One,___ Je - sus.

1st & last time
Fine

2. - sus: your name is like hon - ey on___ my lips,___ your Spi - rit like wa-

- ter to___ my soul; your word is a lamp___ un - to___ my feet-

D.C. al fine

___ Je - sus, I love___ you,___ I love___ you.

82   Jesus, Lover Of My Soul

82a   The Hope Of Glory

from Colossians 1.27

Christ in you, the hope of glory.
This is the gospel we proclaim!

83 Jesus Shall Take The Highest Honour

Chris Bowater

84 Jesus, We Have Heard Your Spirit (*Where You Lead Us*)

Words: Martin E Leckebusch
Music: Ludwig Van Beethoven
Arr. David Ball

84a   The Mission Of The Church

Mark 10: 29-31

"I tell you the truth," Jesus replied, "no-one who has left home or brothers or sisters or mother or father or children or fields for me and the gospel will fail to receive a hundred times as much in this present age (homes, brothers, sisters, mothers, children and fields - and with them, persecutions) and in the age to come, eternal life. But many who are first will be last, and the last first."

85

Jesus, What A Beautiful Name

Tanya Riches

Flowing

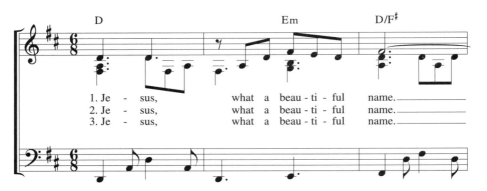

1. Je - sus, what a beau - ti - ful name.
2. Je - sus, what a beau - ti - ful name.
3. Je - sus, what a beau - ti - ful name.

— Son of God, Son of Man, Lamb that was
— Truth re - vealed, my fu - ture sealed, healed my
— Res - cued my soul, my strong - hold, lifts me from

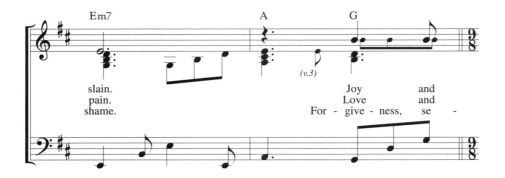

slain.
pain.
shame.

(v.3)

Joy and
Love and
For - give - ness, se -

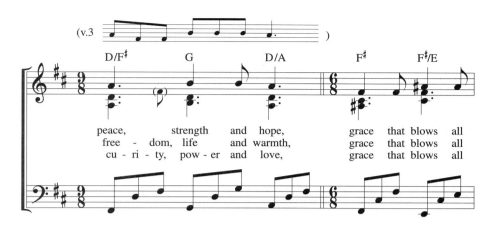

(v.3)

| D/F# | G | D/A | F# | F#/E |

peace,   strength and hope,   grace that blows all
free - dom, life   and warmth,   grace that blows all
cu - ri - ty, pow - er and love,   grace that blows all

| Bm7 | Em7 | D/A | G/A |

fear a - way.   Je - sus,   what a beau - ti - ful
fear a - way.   Je - sus,   what a beau - ti - ful
fear a - way.   Je - sus,   what a beau - ti - ful

| D | Dsus4 | D |

name.
name.
name.

85a   Celtic Night Prayer (1)

Calm me, O Lord, as you stilled the storm.
Still me, O Lord, keep me from harm.
Let all the tumult within me cease.
Enfold me, Lord, in Your peace.

With thanks to the Northumbria Community for permission to use these words from 'A Northumbria Office' © Northumbria Community Trust, Hetton Hall, Chatton, Alnwick, Northumberland, NE66 5SD.

86 King Of Kings, Majesty

Steadily

Jarrod Cooper

Verse

1. King of kings, majesty. God of heaven living in me. Gentle Saviour, closest friend. Strong deliverer, beginning and end. All with-
2. Earth and heaven worship you. Love eternal, faithful and true. Who bought the nations, ransomed souls. Brought this sinner near to your throne. All with-

This song is recorded on the Spring Harvest 1999 New Songs Album.

lyrics under the music:

in me falls at— your throne.
in me cries out— in praise. Your ma - jes -

ty, I can but bow, I lay my all be - fore you

now. In ro - yal robes I don't de -

serve I live to serve your ma - jes - ty.

86a   The Future

Romans 8: 1

Therefore, there is now no condemnation for those who are in Christ Jesus, because through Christ Jesus the law of the Spirit of life set me free from the law of sin and death.

87 Let Everything That Has Breath

Driving

Matt Redman

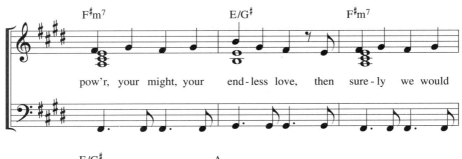

pow'r, your might, your end-less love, then sure-ly we would

ne-ver cease to praise._____

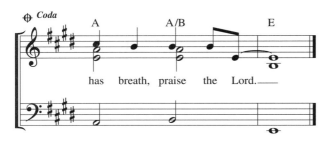

Coda

has breath, praise the Lord._____

87a The Lord Of Every Family

from Ephesians 3.

Let us declare our faith in God

We believe in God the Father,
from whom every family in heaven and on earth is named.
We believe in God the Son,
who lives in our hearts through faith, and fills us with his love.
We believe in God the Holy Spirit,
who strengthens us inwardly with power from on high.
We believe in one God; Father, Son and Holy Spirit.
To him be glory in the church and in Christ Jesus
forever and ever. Amen.

Bridges — From D

221

88 Let The Chimes Of Freedom
Ring (Chimes Of Freedom)

With a lilting feel

Dave Bilbrough

1. Let the chimes of free - dom ring all a - cross the
2. O - pen wide your pri - son doors to greet the Lord of
(3.) ev - ery cor - ner of the earth, to ev - ery tribe and
4. Spread the news and make it plain he breaks the power of
(5.) will re - turn in ma - jes - ty to take his right - ful

earth; lift your voice in praise to him and
life; songs of tri - umph fill the air, Christ
tongue, make known that God so loved this world that he
sin; Je - sus died and rose a - gain, his
place as King of all e - ter - ni - ty, the

sing of all his worth, and sing of all his
Je - sus is a - live, Christ Je - sus is a -
gave his on - ly Son, he gave his on - ly
love will ne - ver end, his love will ne - ver
name a - bove all names, the name a - bove all

worth.
Son.

live.
end.
names.

Let all the peo-ple hear the news of the One who comes to save: he's the Lord of all the u-ni-verse, and for-ev-er he shall reign. 3. In reign. And for-ev-er more, and for-ev-er more, and for-ev-er-more He shall reign. And for- 5. He

89 Let Your Love Come Down

How much pain___ can peo - ple bear?___
It can heal___ the wound - ed soul.___

Are we reap - ing what___ we've sown,___ voic - es si - lent for___
In the streets___ where an - ger reigns,___ love will wash___ a - way___

too long?___ We are call ing, let your love___ come down.___
___ the pain.___ We are call - ing, hea-ven's love___ come down.___

Coda
D.C.   Am   Fine

89a   Families And Relationships
Colossians 3: 16

Let the word of Christ dwell in you richly as you reach and
admonish one another with all wisdom, and as you sing psalms,
hymns and spiritual songs with gratitude in your hearts to God.

90 Lord, For The Years

Words: Timothy Dudley-Smith
Music: Michael Baughen
Arr. Christopher Norton

Medium slow ♩ = 108

1. Lord, for the years your love has kept and guid - ed,
2. Lord, for that word, the word of life which fires us,
3. Lord, for our land, in this our ge - ne - ra - tion,
4. Lord, for our world, when we dis - own and doubt him,
5. Lord, for our - selves; in liv - ing power re - make us -

urged and in - spired us, cheered us on our way,
speaks to our hearts and sets our souls a - blaze,
spi - rits op - pressed by plea - sure, wealth and care;
love - less in strength, and com - fort - less in pain;
self on the cross and Christ up - on the throne,

sought us and saved us, par-doned and pro-vid-ed,
teach-es and trains, re-bukes us and in-spires us;
for young and old, for com-mon-wealth and na-tion,
hun-gry and help-less, lost in-deed with-out him,
past put be-hind us, for the fu-ture take us,

Lord of the years, we bring our thanks to-day.
Lord of the word, re-ceive your peo-ple's praise.
Lord of our land, be pleased to hear our prayer.
Lord of the world, we pray that Christ may reign.
Lord of our lives, to live for Christ a-lone.

90a   Families And Relationships
Ephesians 2: 10

For we are God's workmanship, created in Christ Jesus to do
good works, which God prepared in advance for us to do.

91 Lord, I Am Not My Own
(What I Have Vowed)

Tenderly

Matt Redman

1. Lord, I am not my own, no long-er my own, liv-ing now for you, and ev-ery-thing I think, all I say and do is for you, my Lord.
2. Now tak-ing up the cross, walk-ing on your paths, hold-ing out your truth, run-ning in this race, bow-ing ev-ery day, all for you, my Lord.
3. Earth has no-thing I de-sire that lives out-side of you, I'm con-sumed with you. Trea-sures have no hold, no-thing else will do, on-ly you, my Lord.

92 Lord, I Come To You
(The Power Of Your Love)

Geoff Bullock

♩ = 88

1. Lord, I come to you,— let my heart be changed, re-newed,—
   flow - ing from the grace that I found— in you.

2. Lord, un-veil my eyes,— let me see you face to face,—
   the know-ledge of your love, as you live— in me.

And, Lord, I've come to know—— the weak-ness-es I see in me—— will be stripped a-way——

Lord, re-new my mind—— as your will un-folds in my life,— in liv-ing ev-ery day——

**This song is recorded on the Spring Harvest 1997 Live Worship Album - Volume 1
and on the Double Album Celebrating 20 Years Of Spring Harvest.**

93 Lord, I Lift Your Name

Rick Founds

Lord, I lift your name on high,

Lord, I love to sing your prais-es; I'm so glad you're in my

life, I'm so glad you came to save us.

You came from heav-en to earth to show the way,

from the earth to the cross, my debt to pay,

from the cross to the grave, from the grave to the sky,

Lord, I lift your name on high.

93a   God Sets Us Free

from Colossians

Once in darkness - into light.
Praise the Lord, who sets us free!
Once at enmity - now restored.
Praise the Lord, who sets us free!
Dead in sin - now raised with Christ.
Praise the Lord, who sets us free!
Once without hope - now destined for glory.
Praise the Lord, who sets us free! Praise the Lord!

© Mark Earey

94 Lord Jesus May Your Spirit Come *(Within The Veil)*

Slowly, with a lilting feel

Robin Mark

Lord Je-sus may — your Spi-rit come,
make this a ho-ly place, for we have longed to
gaze up-on the glo-ry of your — face. —
Then ev-ery sel-fish will ex-posed, and ev-ery vain — de-

sire, are hum-bled and then pu-ri-fied by your ho-ly, ho - ly_____ fire.

(Fine)

Verse

O_ Lamb of_ God,_ the glo-ry of_ your_ name,_____ per-fect_ in ho - li-ness, and pur - est love,_

and in that love___ we'll

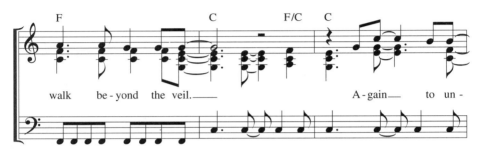

walk be-yond the veil.___ A-gain___ to un-

der-stand___ what you have done.___

D.S. al fine | **To end**

94a   Offertory Prayer

**Heavenly Father,
let these gifts go where we cannot go,
and help those whom we cannot reach;
through them
let the unlearned be taught,
the hungry fed,
the sick healed
and the lost found;
for Jesus' sake. Amen.**

95   Lord Of The Dance

With life

Kevin Prosch

96 Lord, You Have My Heart

Martin Smith

241

97 Love, Joy, Peace
(The Fruit Of The Spirit)

David Lyle Morris

Rhythmically

Love, joy, peace—— and pa - tience, kind-ness, good-ness, faith-ful - ness,—— gen - tle-ness—— and self—— con - trol:——

1. this is the fruit of—— the Spi - rit. We want the fruit of—— the Spi - rit.

2. we will reap what—— we sow,——

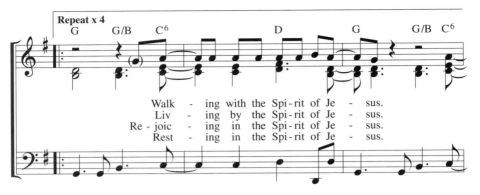

Walk - ing with the Spi - rit of Je - sus.
Liv - ing by the Spi - rit of Je - sus.
Re - joic - ing in the Spi - rit of Je - sus.
Rest - ing in the Spi - rit of Je - sus.

97a   In Days To Come
Call to worship adapted from Isaiah 2 & 11

Leader: In days to come,
the mountain of the Lord's house
will be set over all other mountains,
raised high above all hills.

Nations will stream towards it
and many peoples will say,

ALL: LET US GO UP TO THE MOUTAIN OF THE LORD
TO THE HOUSE OF THE GOD OF JACOB,
THAT HE MAY TEACH US HIS WAYS,
AND THAT WE MAY WALK IN HIS PATHS.

Leader: Instruction comes from Jerusalem,
ALL: THE WORD OF THE LORD, FROM ZION.

98 Make Us A House Of Prayer
(House Of Prayer)

Moderately

Judy Gresham

Make us a house of prayer that ma - ny would come and find you here, make us a house of prayer, Lord, to the glo - ry ——— of your name

Coda

name.

We're on our knees be-fore___ you
We're on our knees be-fore___ you

to wor-ship and a-dore___ you, we long to see you move in
to cry out and im-plore___ you to save our dy-ing na-tion

1.
power.

2.
now. Have mer-cy, Lord,___ have

mer-cy, Lord,___ have___ mer-cy___ on our land. Have land.___

99 Many Are The Words
(Now To Live The Life)

Steadily

Matt Redman

1. Ma - ny are the words we speak, (v.2 we pray that)
(2.) Pre - cious are the words we speak,

ma - ny are the songs we sing;
pre - cious are the songs we sing;

ma - ny kinds of of-fer-ings, but now to live the life.
pre - cious all these of-fer-ings, but now to live the life.

1. *(Repeat v.1)*

This song is recorded on the Spring Harvest 1999 Praise Mix.

250

Now to live— the life,—

now to live— the life,—

now to live— the life,—

now to live the life.

99a   Living As Families

God our Father,
your Son Jesus Christ lived in a family at Nazareth
grant that in our families on earth
we may so learn to love and to live together
that we may rejoice as one family in your heavenly home;
through Jesus Christ our Lord. Amen.

© Church Family Worship (Hodder & Stoughton, 1986). © Jubilate Hymns Ltd. 1986 (No.193)
from The Alternative Prayer Book 1984, Church of Ireland

100 Men Of Faith

♩ = 100

Martin Smith

1. Men of faith, rise up and sing of the great and glor-ious
(2) wo-men of the truth, stand and sing to bro-ken
(3) church with bro-ken wings; fill this place with songs a-

King; you are strong when you feel weak, in your bro-ken-ness com-
hearts, who can know the heal-ing power of our glor-ious King of
gain, of our God who reigns on high: by his grace a-gain we'll

plete._____ Shout to the
love._____
fly._____

north and the south, sing to the east and the west:

'Je - sus is sa- viour to all, Lord of hea- ven and

earth.'———

2. Rise up
3. Rise up

We've been through fire,—— we've been through rain; we've been re-fined by the

power of his name. We've fal- len deep- er in love with you,

you've burned the truth on our lips.———

253

Lord of hea-ven and earth, Lord of hea-ven and

earth, Lord of hea-ven and earth.

100a The Song Of Moses And Miriam
from Exodus 15

I will sing to the Lord, for he has triumphed gloriously:
he has thrown the horse and its rider into the sea.

The Lord is my strength and my song:
and he has become my salvation.

This is my God, and I will praise him:
the God of my forebears and I will exalt him.

Lord, who among the gods is like you:
majestic in holiness and working wonders?

In your unfailing love you will lead the people you have redeemed:
in your strength you will guide them to your holy dwelling.

You will bring them in and plant them on your mountain:
the place you have made for your dwelling.

In the sanctuary that your hands have established:
you, Lord, will reign for ever and ever.

Patterns for Worship (Church House Publishing, 1995).

Bridges — From F

To B♭

To C

To D

To E♭

To G

255

101 My First Love
(Like A Child)

As a jig

Stuart Townend

1. My first love is a blaz-ing fi-re, I feel his power-ful
2. My first love is a rush-ing riv-er, a wa-ter-fall that will
3. Re-store the years of the chur-ch's slum-ber, re-vive the fire that has

love in me; for he has kin-dled a flame of pas-sion,
nev-er cease; and in the tor-rent of tears and laugh-ter,
grown so dim; re-new the love of those first en-coun-ters,

and I will let it grow in me. And in the night I will
I feel a heal-ing power re-leased. And I will draw from your
that we may come a-live a-gain. And we will rise like the

sing your praise, my love.
well of life, my love,
dawn through-out the earth,

And in the morn-ing I'll seek your face, my love.
and in your grace I'll be sa-tis-fied, my love.
un-til the trum-pet an-noun-ces your re-turn.

Chorus
And like a child I will dance in your pres-ence,
O, let the joy of hea-ven pour down on me. I still re-mem-ber the
first day I met you, and I don't ev-er want to lose that fire, my first
love.

102 My Heart Is Full
(All the Glory)

From Hebrews 1
Graham Kendrick

Moderate ♩ = 65

1. My heart is full of ad-mi-ra-tion for you, my Lord, my God and King; your ex-cel-lence my in-spi-ra-tion, your words of grace have made my spi-rit sing. 2. You love what's

you; Jesus, Saviour,

anointed One, I worship you, I worship

1. you. 3. Your throne, O 2. you.

All the glory, honour and power belong to

you, belong to you;

Je - sus, Sav - iour, a - noint - ed One, I wor - ship you, I wor - ship you; I wor - ship you, I wor - ship you.

102a   All That I Am

All that I am, Lord, I place into Your hands;
all that I do, Lord, I place into Your hands.
Everything I work for, I place into Your hands;
everything I hope for, I place into Your hands.
The troubles that weary me I place into Your hands;
the thoughts that disturb me I place into Your hands.
Each that I pray for I place into Your hands;
each that I care for I place into Your hands.

With thanks to the Northumbria Community for permission to use these words from 'A Northumbrian Office' © Northumbria Community Trust, Hetton Hall, Chatton, Alnwick, Northumberland, NE66 5SD.

103 My Jesus, My Saviour
(Shout To The Lord)

Darlene Zschech

This song is recorded on the Double Album Celebrating 20 Years Of Spring Harvest.

264

will roar____ at the sound_____ of your name._____ I sing for joy____ at the work____ of your hands,____ for - ev - er I'll love____ you, for - ev - er I'll stand;____ no - thing com - pares____ to the prom - ise I have____ in____ you._____

104   Name Of All Majesty

Words: Timothy Dudley-Smith
Music: Michael Baughen
Arr. Noël Tredinnick

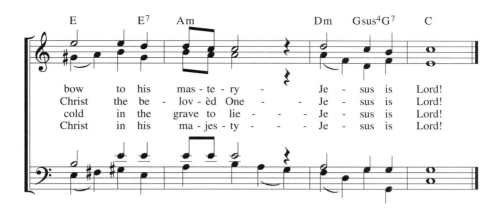

| | E | E7 | Am | | Dm | Gsus4G7 | C |

bow to his mas - te - ry -   Je - sus is Lord!
Christ the be - lov - èd One - - Je - sus is Lord!
cold in the grave to lie - - - Je - sus is Lord!
Christ in his ma - jes - ty - - - Je - sus is Lord!

104a At The End Of Time
from Mark 13

When the skies grow dark and buildings fall, then hear us Lord:
have mercy on us.

When the deceivers come and the nations rise in anger,
then hear us, Lord:
have mercy on us.

When the famines begin, and when the earth shakes to bring
the future to birth, then hear us, Lord:
have mercy on us.

When we stand for a witness, when we are arrested and betrayed,
then hear us, Lord:
have mercy on us.

When the sun is darkened and the moon fails to give us light,
and the stars fall from the sky, then hear us, Lord:
have mercy on us.

When you come in your great power and glory with your angels
from heaven;
have mercy, Lord:
gather us from the four winds
from the ends of the earth
to be with you for ever. Amen.

Bible Praying, Michael Perry (HarperCollins, 1992). © Michael Perry 1992.

105 No Scenes Of Stately Majesty

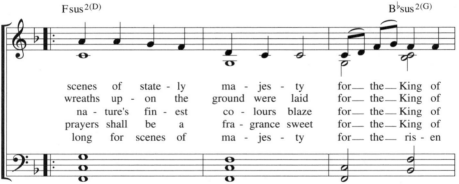

scenes of state - ly ma - jes - ty for the King of
wreaths up - on the ground were laid for the King of
na - ture's fin - est co - lours blaze for the King of
prayers shall be a fra - grance sweet for the King of
long for scenes of ma - jes - ty for the ris - en

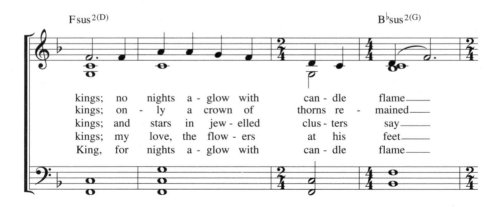

kings; no nights a - glow with can - dle flame___
kings; on - ly a crown of thorns re - mained___
kings; and stars in jew - elled clus - ters say___
kings; my love, the flow - ers at his feet___
King, for nights a - glow with can - dle flame___

This song is recorded on the Spring Harvest 1998 Live Worship Album.

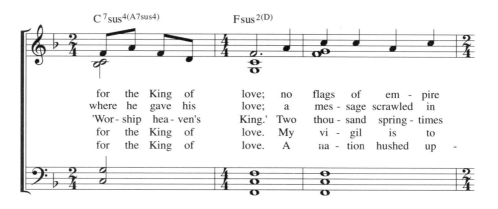

for the King of love; no flags of em - pire
where he gave his love; a mes - sage scrawled in
'Wor - ship hea - ven's King.' Two thou - sand spring - times
for the King of love. My vi - gil is to
for the King of love. A na - tion hushed up -

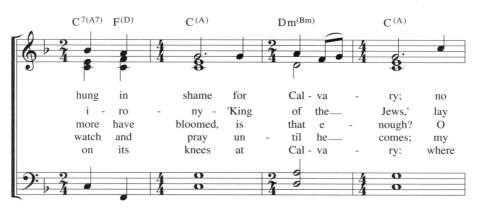

hung in shame for Cal - va - ry; no
i - ro - ny - 'King of the_ Jews,' lay
more have bloomed, is that e - nough? O
watch and pray un - til he_ comes; my
on its knees at Cal - va - ry: where

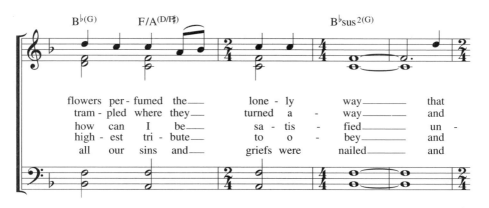

flowers per - fumed the_ lone - ly way_ that
tram - pled where they_ turned a - way_ and
how can I be_ sa - tis - fied_ un -
high - est tri - bute_ to o - bey_ and
all our sins and_ griefs were nailed_ and

269

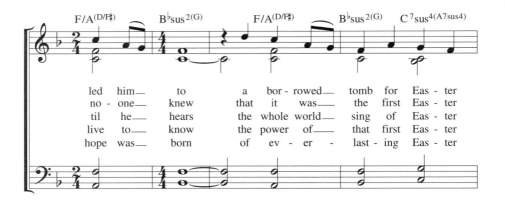

led him— to a bor-rowed— tomb for Eas-ter
no-one— knew that it was— the first Eas-ter
til he— hears the whole world— sing of Eas-ter
live to— know the power of— that first Eas-ter
hope was— born of ev-er - last-ing Eas-ter

Day.
Day.
love.
Day.
Day.

2. No
3. Yet
4. My
5. I

105a   God's Foolish Wisdom

We praise you Jesus, for the way you came to us;
not as a ruler; but loving and serving us.
This is the stumbling block - Jesus our Lord!

We praise you Jesus, for the way you died for us;
you did no wrong; yet you died on the cross for us.
This is the stumbling block - Jesus our Lord!

We praise you Jesus, for crushing the pride in us;
we could not earn what you gave as a gift to us.
This is the stumbling block - Jesus our Lord!

We praise you Jesus, for showing God's plan to us;
foolish to many, God's wisdom walked here with us.
This is the stumbling block - Jesus our Lord!

106 No Stone Left On Another

Words:Christopher Idle
Music:David Jenkins
arr. David Ball

Je - sus has to tell:_____ the
know who will be - tray;_____ but
pared to call him friend?_____ His
no - thing stays the same;_____ this
heav'n is soon to be,_____ in

on - ly path to glo - ry,_____ a -
when they cru - ci - fy him_____ all
blood is shed for ma - ny;_____ his
Je - sus - he is ri - sen!_____ He
Je - sus we are learn - ing_____ the

(Fine)

cross____ the brink of hell._____
hell____ is on dis - play._____
king - dom seems to end._____
comes,____ and speaks my name._____
songs____ of vic - to - ry._____

273

107 Nothing Can Keep Me From His Love

Geoff Baker

♩ = 112

No-thing can keep me from his love that shines through the dark-est night. No e-ne-my be-low, a-bove can tri-umph a-gainst his might. So in my weak-ness I am strong, with Christ my shield and Christ my song. All the ri-vers,

108 Not With Eloquent Words
(The Power Of The Cross)

With a latin feel

Robin Mark

Not____ with e - lo - quent words,
Love____ is stron - ger than death,

not____ a life - style de - sire,
lives____ re - fined as pure gold,

this____ is the wis - dom of God,
hearts____ put to the test

this is his
fast to the

Spi - - - rit's fire.
Sa - - - viour hold.

Mer - cies that ne - ver

end, so shall my heart de - pend. On the

Chorus

power_____ of the__ cross,

lift - ed me_____ when I__ was lost:___

— I will not_____

277

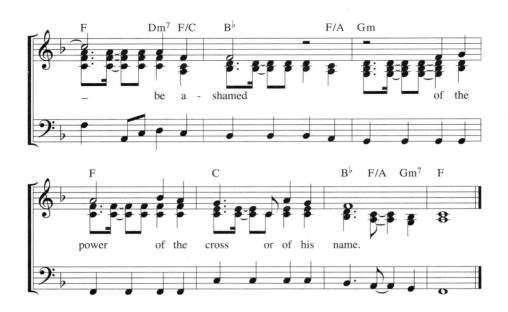

be a - shamed of the
power of the cross or of his name.

108a One Thing I Seek
from Psalm 27 and Mark 1

**One thing I have asked of the Lord,
this is what I seek
that I may dwell in the house of the Lord
all the days of my life;
to behold the beauty of the Lord
and to seek him in his temple.**

Who is it that you seek? **We seek the Lord our God.**

Do you seek him with all your heart? **We do. Lord have mercy.**

Do you seek him with all your soul? **We do. Lord have mercy.**

Do you seek him with all your mind? **We do. Lord have mercy.**

Do you seek him with all your strength? **We do. Lord have mercy.**

**The Lord is our light and our salvation; whom shall we fear?
The Lord is the stronghold of our lives; we shall not be afraid.
Amen.**

109 O Adoramus Te Domine
(We Adore You, Lord Jesus Christ)

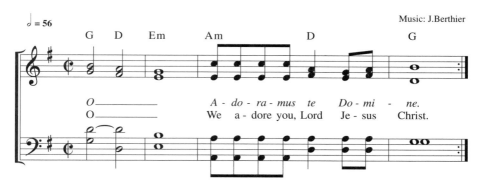

♩ = 56   Music: J.Berthier

O_____ A - do - ra - mus te Do - mi - ne.
O_____ We a - dore you, Lord Je - sus Christ.

This song is recorded on the Spring Harvest 1997 Live Worship Album - Volume 2.

109a Longing For Blessing
from Exodus 15 & 20 v 24

During a time of worship

Leader   Listen to the words of the Lord.
'Wherever I cause my name to be honoured -
I will come to you and bless you.'
(silence)
Let us stand together and pray.

All   **Holy God,**
noone compares to You.
Majestic God.
Awesome God.
Wonderful God.
Holy God.
Your name, Saviour, we worship.

Leader   These words must reflect our hearts desire -
to honour Him.
In the quiet tell God of your intention
to crown Him, undisputed King, in your life.
(silence)
Repeat the prayer together.

110 O God Beyond All Praising

Words: Michael Perry
Music: Gustav Holst
arr. Christopher Norton

With dignity ♩ = 98

1. O— God be-yond all prais-ing, we wor-ship you to-
2. Then— hear, O gra-cious Sav-iour, ac-cept the love we

day and— sing the love a-maz-ing that songs can-not re-
bring, that— we who know your fa-vour may serve you as our

pay; for— we can on-ly won-der at— ev-ery gift you
king; and— whe-ther our to-mor-rows be— filled with good or

111   O Righteous God

With awe

Mal Pope

1. O righ-teous God who search-es minds and hearts,
2. O Lord my God, I take re-fuge in you;

bring to an end the vio-lence of my foes,
save and de-li-ver me from all my foes.

and make the righ-teous— more se-cure, O— righ-
My shield is God the— Lord most high, O— Lord—

teous God.
— my God.

Sing praise to the name of the

This song is recorded on the **Spring Harvest 1997 Live Worship Album - Volume 1**
and the 1999 New Songs Album.

Lord most high. Sing praise to the name of the Lord most high. Give thanks to the Lord who rescues me, O righteous God.

111a Leaders

1 Timothy 2: 1-4

I urge, then, first of all, that requests, prayers, intercession and thanksgiving be made for everyone - for kings and all those in authority, that we may live peaceful and quiet lives in all godliness and holiness. This is good, and pleases God our Saviour, who wants all men to be saved and to come to a knowledge of the truth.

112 Oh Our Lord And King
(King Forever)

With strength

Alan Rose

Oh our Lord and King, our praise to you____ we bring,____
Seat-ed high a-bove,____ you are the one____ we love,____

there is no o-ther Rock____ but you.
this is our song of praise____ to

you.

1. King for - ev - er!
2. Who is like you?
3. Ab - ba Fa - ther,

you are the First and you're the Last.
Who else is wor - thy of our_____ praise?
your stead - fast love will ne - ver_____ fail.

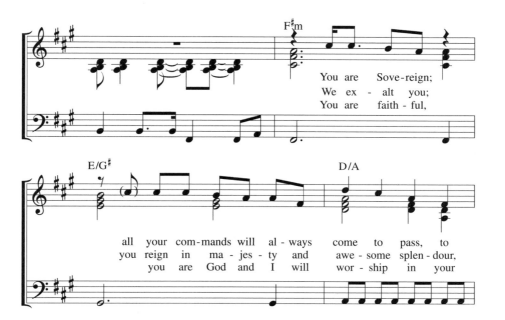

You are Sove-reign;
We ex - alt you;
You are faith-ful,

all your com-mands will al - ways come to pass, to
you reign in ma - jes - ty and awe - some splen - dour,
you are God and I will wor - ship in your

D.C. al fine

give you glo - ry!
King for - ev - er!
courts for - ev - er.

112a   United To The Love Of Christ
from Romans 8

What can separate us from the love of Christ?
Nothing can separate us from the love of Christ!
Can trouble do it?   **No!**
Can hardship do it?   **No!**
Can persecution do it? **No!**
Can hunger do it?   **No!**
Can poverty do it?   **No!**
Can danger do it?   **No!**
Can death do it?   **No!**
So what can separate us from the love of Christ?
Nothing can! Alleluia!

from Scripture Union SALT material

113 O Your Hands Of Kindness
(Hands Of Kindness)

1. O, your hands of kind-ness are here for me, and I've heard they are silk-en and can car-ry me.
2. O, your hands of mer-cy were scarred for me, and your bo-dy was bro-ken so that I go free.
3. O, your love that burns me, deep-er than the sea, and the trea-sure I find here: the Sa-viour's love for me.

Chorus
How I love you, all I am is you, King of love I bow.

114 Oh The Lord Our God Is Mighty

D Lyon & J Markin

Oh the Lord our God is migh-ty, his name ex-alt-ed o-ver all: oh the Lord our God is ho-ly, come now and praise

288

114a   Families And Relationships

Ephesians 4: 11-13

It was he who gave some to be apostles, some to be prophets, some to be evangelists, and some to be pastors and teachers, to prepare God's people for works of service, so that the body of Christ may be built up until we all reach unity in the faith and in the knowledge of the Son of God and become mature, attaining to the whole measure of the fulness of Christ.

115   Oh, The Mercy Of God

Flowing

Geoff Bullock

1. Oh, the mer - cy of God,—— the glo - ry of
2. Oh, the rich - ness of grace,—— the depths of his
3. Oh, the glo - ry of God—— ex - pressed in his

grace, that you chose to re - deem us, to for-
love, in—— him is re - demp - tion, the for-
Son, his—— i - mage and like - ness re -

give and re - store, and you call us your chil - dren,——
give - ness of sin. You—— called us as right - eous, pre-
vealed to us all; the—— plea of the a - ges com-

chosen in him to be ho-ly and blame-less to the
des-tined in him for the praise of his glo-ry,— in-
plet-ed in Christ, that— we be pre-sent-ed per-

Chorus

glo-ry of God. To the praise of his glo-ri-ous
clud-ed in Christ. }
fect-ed in him. }

grace, to the praise of his glo-ry and power;

to him be all glo-ry, ho-nour and praise

for-ev-er and ev-er and ev-er, a-men.

116 On The Bloodstained Ground *(I Kneel Down)*

Steadily

Graham Kendrick

1. On the blood - stained ground,— where the sha - dow falls.—
   (2.) lift my eyes— to a tear - stained face.—
   way my shame,— my— pain, my pride,—
   wash the stains— of my guil - ty heart—

Of a cross— and a crown of thorns,—
Who is this,— dy - ing in my place?—
'till I'm clean— in ev - ery part—
ev - ery sin— that I once de - nied—

I kneel down, I kneel down I—
Wash a -

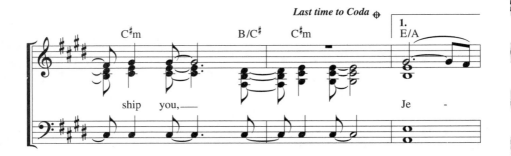

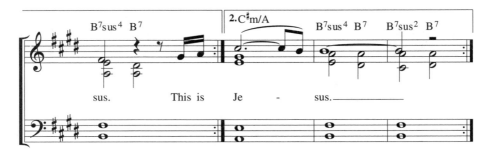

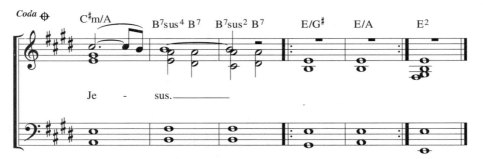

116a Families And Relationships
Matthew 18: 2-6

He called a little child and had him stand among them. And he said: " I tell you the truth, unless you change and become like little children, you will never enter the kingdom of heaven. Therefore whoever humbles himself like this child is the greatest in the kingdom of heaven. And whoever welcomes a little child like this in my name welcomes me. But if anyone causes one of these little ones who believe in me to sin, it would be better for him to have a large millstone hung around his neck and to be drowned in the depths of the sea."

117 One Lord, One Faith
(Increase In Me)

Steadily

Steve & Velveta Thompson
& Andy Mitchell

1. One Lord, one faith, we stand to-ge-ther. One God and Fa-ther of us all. In u-ni-ty and by God's Spi-rit, we walk as one

2. To reach the lost is our com-mis-sion, to stretch our hands to those in need: re-flect God's heart, ful-fil his call-ing and then his king-

to reach our goal.
dom will in - crease.

Chorus

In - crease in me the flame that's burn - ing.

Ig - nite in us the pas - sion for the lost.

En - large our hearts, the

118 Only By Grace

Gerrit Gufstafson

Gently ♩ = 90

On - ly by grace— can we en - ter,— on - ly by grace— we can stand:— not by our hu - man en-dea- - vour, but by the blood— of the Lamb.— In - to your pre - sence you call— us,— you call— us to come.— In - to your pre - sence you draw— us,— and

now by your grace— we come,— now by your grace— we come.—

Fine

Lord, if you mark— our trans-gres-

—sions, who would stand?

Thanks to your grace— we are cleansed— by the blood— of the Lamb.

1.

2. *D.C. al fine*

119   Our God Is Great

Bright and rhythmic

Dave Bilbrough

Our God is great, our God is great, our God is great, our God is great.

1.3.5.7. Our God is

2.4.8. (Fine) **Verse**

1. He
2. The

gave us— the wind, the sun and— the snow, the sand on— the sea shore,. the
gifts that— he brings are new ev - ery day, from glo - ri - ous sun - set— to

This song is recorded on the Spring Harvest 1998 Live Worship Album.

flow - ers— that grow, morn - ing— and eve - ning,
soft fal - ling rain, the mist on— the hills, the

win - ter— and spring; come join all— cre - a - tion— and
light and— the shade; come join all— cre - a - tion— in

sing. Our God is For
praise.

mu- sic— and dan-cing,—the sounds that— we hear; for co-lours—and words, the

life that— we share,—— we say: Our God is

301

120 Over All The Earth
(Lord, Reign In Me)

Brenton Brown

1. Ov-er all the earth, you reign on high,
   ev-ery moun-tain stream, every sun-set sky.
   But my one re-quest, Lord, my on-ly aim
   is that you'd reign in me a-gain.

2. Ov-er ev-ery thought, ov-er ev-ery word,
   may my life re-flect the beau-ty of my Lord;
   'cause you mean more to me than a-ny earth-ly thing.
   So won't you reign in me a-gain.

This song is recorded on the Spring Harvest 1999 New Songs Album.

2. C   **D.S. (to Chorus)**   *Coda*   **F**   **G**   **Dm⁷**

Lord, reign in — me, reign in me a - gain, —

F   **G**   **F/G Dm⁷**

won't you reign in me a - gain, —

F   **G**   **C**

won't you reign in me a - gain.

120a   Security
Psalm 127: 1-2

Unless the Lord builds the house,
    its builders labour in vain.
Unless the Lord watches over the city,
    the watchmen stand guard in vain.
In vain you rise early
    and stay up late,
toiling for food to eat -
    for he grants sleep to those he loves.

121 Praise God From Whom All Blessings Flow

Andy Piercy & Dave Clifton
Arr. Alison Berry

Steady Rock ♩ = 132

Praise God from whom— all bless - ings flow,— praise him all crea - tures here— be - low.— Praise him a- bove— you hea- venly host,— praise Fa - ther, Son— and Ho - ly Ghost.— Praise - ly Ghost.— Give glo - ry to the Fa - ther,— give

1.,5.,7. *3rd time to bridge.*
Last time to Coda ✛

2.,4.,6.

121a Declaration Of Faith

To whom shall we go?
You have the words of eternal life,
and we have believed and have come to know
that You are the Holy One of God.
Praise to You, Lord Jesus Christ, King of Endless glory.

With thanks to the Northumbria Community for permission to use these words from 'A Northumbrian Office' © Northumbria Community Trust, Hetton Hall, Chatton, Alnwick, Northumberland, NE66 5SD.

122 Praise, My Soul

Words: from Psalm 103
Henry Francis Lyte
Music: John Goss
Arr. David Peacock

With strength ♩ = 102

1. Praise, my soul, the king of hea - ven; to his feet your tri - bute bring! Ran - somed, healed, re - stored, for - gi - ven,
2. Praise him for his grace and fa - vour to our fa - thers in dis - tress; praise him still the same as ev - er,
3. Fa - ther - like he tends and spares us; all our hopes and fears he knows, in his hands he gent - ly bears us,
4. An - gels, help us to a - dore him - you be - hold him face to face; sun and moon, bow down be - fore him -

This song is recorded on the Spring Harvest 1997 Live Worship Album - Volume 2.

123 Salvation Belongs To Our God

Adrian Howard
& Pat Turner

This song is recorded on the Double Album Celebrating 20 Years Of Spring Harvest.

ev - er and ev - er, be to our God for ev - er and ev - er,

be to our God for ev - er and ev - er! A -

- men. 2. And

1.

2. D.S.

123a The Lord's Prayer

Our Father in heaven,
hallowed be your name,
your kingdom come,
your will be done
　　on earth as in heaven.
Give us today our daily bread.
Forgive us our sins,
　　as we forgive those who sin against us.
Lead us not into temptation,
but deliver us from evil,
for the kingdom, the power and the glory are yours,
now and forever, Amen.

124   Search Me

Ian Mizen
& Andy Pressdee

Steadily

Search me,— O God, and know my—heart,— lead me in your ways for-ev-er.   *(1x)* I want to be—— ho—ly, giv-ing ev-ery-thing— to— you,—

This song is recorded on the Spring Harvest 1999 Praise Mix.

I want to be____ pure in__ heart__ and__ pure__ in__ mind,__ I want to be____ ho - ly, al - ways__ pleas - ing__ you,____ I want to live__ for_____ you.____

125 Sound The Trumpet

Dave Bilbrough

Strong and rhythmic

Sound the trum-pet, strike the drum, see the King of glo-ry come, join the prai-ses ris-ing from the peo-ple of the Lord.

Let your voic-es now be heard, un-re-strained and un-re-served. Pre-pare the way— for his re-turn,— you peo-ple of the Lord. Sing, 'Je-sus is

This song is recorded on the Spring Harvest 1998 Live Worship Album.

Lord, Je-sus is— Lord.' _____ Bow

down to his au-tho-ri-ty, for he has slain the

en-e-my; of heav'n and hell he holds the key;

Je-sus is Lord, Je-sus is— Lord. _____

126 Standing In Your Presence
(I Live To Know You)

Building, with strength

Darlene Zschech

1. Stand - ing— in your pre-sence,— Lord, my heart and life are changed;—
(2.) called me,— I will fol - low;— your will for me I'm sure.—

— just to love you— and to live to— see your
Let your heart - beat— be my heart's cry,— let me

beau - ty and your grace.— } Hea - ven and earth— cry out— your name,—
live to serve your call.— }

na - tions rise up— and see— your face;—

— and your king - dom is— es - tab - lished— as I

This song is recorded on the Spring Harvest 1999 New Songs Album.

127 Surely Our God
(Revealer Of Mysteries)

Moderately

David & Liz Morris

Chorus: Sure-ly our God is the God of gods, and the Lord of kings, the re-veal-er of mys-te-ries. Sure-ly our God is the God of gods, and the Lord of kings, the re-veal-er of mys-ter-ies.

Verse (Fine)
1. He chan-ges the times and the
2. I'll praise you al-ways my
3. Thank you for send-ing your

This song is recorded on the Spring Harvest 1997 New Songs Album.

sea - sons, he gives rhy - thm to— the tides, he
Fa - ther, you are Lord of hea - ven and earth. You
on - ly Son, we may know the mys-tery of God; he

knows what is hid - den in the dark - est of pla - ces, brings the
hide— your se - crets from the 'wise' and the learn - ed, and re -
o - pens the trea - sures of— wis - dom and know - ledge to the

sha - dows in - to his— light.
veal them to this, your— child.
hum - ble, not to the— proud.

127a Invocation Of The Holy Spirit

Most powerful Holy Spirit, come down upon us
and subdue us.

From Heaven, where the ordinary
is made glorious, and glory seems
but ordinary,
bathe us with the brilliance of your light like dew.

With thanks to the Northumbria Community for permission to use these words from 'A Northumbrian Office' © Northumbria Community Trust, Hetton Hall, Chatton, Alnwick, Northumberland, NE66 5SD.

128   Tell The World

Dave Bilbrough

Tell the world that Jesus is risen, let his praise encircle the globe; make it known among all the nations that Jesus is alive!

1. From the cradle to the grave, from a stable to a cross;—
2. No eye—has seen,—no ear—has heard—what he's—prepared;

This song is recorded on the Spring Harvest 1998 New Songs Album.

his life was of-fered up in sac-ri-fice_____ for us.
his re-su-rec-tion means his life is ours_____ to share.

He came from hea-ven's throne to seek and save the lost;_____ to
The great-est mi-ra-cle of all has tak-en place;_____

re-con-cile us back to God._____
Christ has ris-en - he is Lord._____

Coda

129 Thank You For Saving Me

With a steady rhythm ♩ = 100

Martin Smith

1. Thank you for sa - ving me; what— can I— say?
You are my ev - ery - thing, I will sing your praise.
You shed your blood for me— what— can I— say?
You took my sin and shame, a sin - ner called by name.—

2. Mer - cy and grace are mine, for - giv - en is my— sin -
Je - sus, my on - ly hope, the Sav - iour of the world.
'Great is the Lord,' we cry, 'God, let your king - dom— come!'
Your word has let me see, thank you for sav - ing me.—

Great is the— Lord,_____ great is the— Lord! For we know your truth has set us free - you've set your hope in me._____ Thank you for sa - ving me what— can I say?

130 The Lord's My Shepherd

Thoughtfully
Capo 1 (D)

Stuart Townend

(Descant) I will trust, I will trust in you.

1. The Lord's my Shep - herd, I'll not want. He makes me
And I will trust in You a - lone. And I will
2. He guides my ways in right-eous - ness, and he a -
3. And though I walk the dark - est path, I will not

I will trust, I will trust in you.

lie in pas - tures green. He leads me
trust in You a - lone, for Your
noints my head with oil, and my
fear the e - vil one, for you are

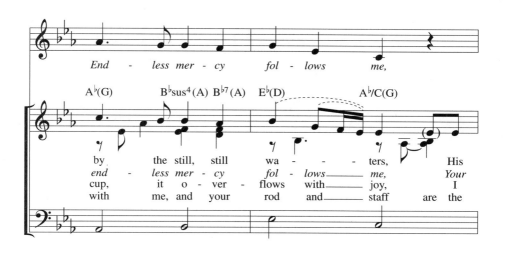

Endless mercy follows me,

A♭(G) B♭sus⁴(A) B♭⁷(A) E♭(D) A♭/C(G)

by the still, still wa - - - ters, His
end - less mer - cy fol - lows me, Your
cup, it o - ver - flows with joy, I
with me, and your rod and staff are the

good - ness will lead me home.

Fm7(Em) B♭sus⁴(A) B♭⁷(A) E♭(D)

good - ness re - stores my soul.
good - ness will lead me home.
feast on his pure de - lights.
com - fort I need to know.

130a   To Know Christ More

Lord Jesus Christ,
we thank you for all the benefits you have won for us,
for all the pains and insults you have borne for us.
Most merciful redeemer,
friend and brother,
may we know you more clearly,
love you more dearly,
and follow you more nearly,
day by day. Amen.

St Richard of Chichester, 1197-1253

131 The Waves Are Breaking
(To The Ends Of The Earth)

Dave Bilbrough

With anticipation

1. The waves are break - ing, the tide is turn - ing, God's Spi - rit is com - ing to this earth; the har - vest is wait - ing, and we have been called to go to the na - tions of this hear,

2. The fire is fal - ling, the wind is blow - ing, the flame is spread - ing a - cross our land; re - vi - val is com - ing, let the world tell ev - ery wo - man, child and

3. The drums are beat - ing, the trum - pet is sound - ing, a war - ri - or spi - rit he's put in our hearts; in the name of the Fa - ther, Spi - rit and Son, we'll take this word to ev - ery - one.

This song is recorded on the Spring Harvest 1999 Praise Mix.

131a The Mission Of The Church
Luke 10: 2-4

He told them, "The harvest is plentiful, but the workers are few. Ask the Lord of the harvest, therfore, to send out workers into his harvest field. Go! I am sending you out like lambs among wolves. Do not take a purse or bag or sandals; and do not greet anyone on the road."

132 The King Of Love
(The King Has Come)

With life
Capo 3 (D)

Stuart Townend
& Kevin Jamieson

329

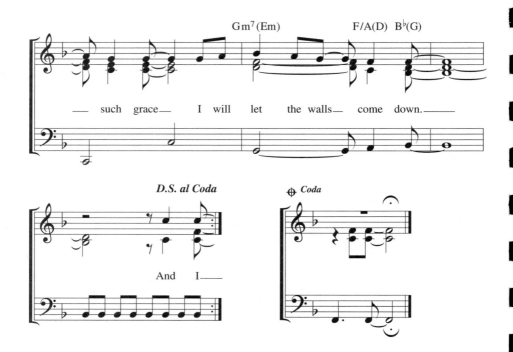

such grace— I will let the walls— come down.—

D.S. al Coda

And I—

Coda

132a   The Apostles' Creed

I believe in God, the Father almighty,
creator of heaven and earth.
I believe in Jesus Christ, his only Son, our Lord.
He was conceived by the power of the Holy Spirit
and born of the Virgin Mary.
He suffered under Pontius Pilate,
was crucified, died and was buried.
On the third day he rose again.
He ascended into heaven,
and is seated at the right hand of the Father.
He will come again to judge the living and the dead.
I believe in the Holy Spirit, the holy catholic Church,
the communion of the saints, the forgiveness of sins,
the resurrection of the body, and the life everlasting.
Amen.

133

There's A Place
(Because Of You)

Strong and rhythmic

Paul Oakley

1. There's— a place where— the streets shine with— the
(2.) pain, no— more sad - ness, no— more
3. There— is joy ev - er - last - ing, there— is

glo - ry of— the Lamb. There's— a
suffer - ing, no— more tears, no— more
glad - ness, there— is peace, there— is

way we— can go there, we— can
sin, no— more sick - ness, no— in
wine ev - er - flow - ing, there's— a

1.

live there be - yond time. Be - cause of— you,

To next section

This song is recorded on the Spring Harvest 1998 New Songs Album.

- er.   Now   we   have   this   hope,___   be- cause   of   you.___

___   Oh,___   we'll   see   You   face   to   face,___

___   and   we   will   dance___   to- geth   -   er   in   the

ci - ty   of___   our   God,___   be- cause   of___   you.

(Fine)   *D.C. verse 3*

134 These Are The Days Of Elijah
(Days Of Elijah)

Robin Mark

1. These are the days of Elijah, declaring the word of the
2. These are the days of Ezekiel, the dry bones becoming as

Lord; and these are the days of your servant, Moses,
flesh; and these are the days of your servant, David, re-

right-eous-ness be-ing re-stored. And though these are days of great
build-ing the tem-ple of praise. These are the days of the

tri-al, of fam-ine and dark-ness and sword, still
har-vest, the fields are as white in the world, and

This song is recorded on the Spring Harvest 1997 New Songs Album, the 1997 Live Worship Album - Volume 1 and on the Double Album Celebrating 20 Years Of Spring Harvest.

we are—the voice in— the des-ert cry-ing 'Pre-pare ye— the way of— the
we are— the la-bour-ers in yourvine-yard, de-clar-ing— the word of— the

Lord.' Be-hold he comes rid-ing on— the clouds, shin-ing like— the
Lord.

sun at the trum-pet call; lift your voice it's the year of ju-bi-

lee, out of Zi - on's hill sal - va - tion comes.

To end

335

135 This Is My Desire
(I Give You My Heart)

Reuben Morgan

This is my — de - sire, — to hon - our
All I have — with - in — me, — I give

you: Lord, with all — my heart — I wor - ship you.
praise: all that I — a - dore — is in you.

Lord, I give you my heart, — I give you my — soul; I

live for you a-lone. Ev-ery breath that I___ take,___

___ ev-ery mo-ment I'm___ a-wake;___ Lord,

1. have your way in me.___

2. have your way in me. 3. have your way in me.___

136 This Is The Place
(Holy Ground)

Dave Bilbrough

1. This is the place where dreams are found;
   where vi-sion comes called ho-ly ground.

2. Your fi-re burns but nev-er dies;
   I re-al-ise this is ho-ly ground.

3. The great I Am re-vealed to man,
   take off your shoes, this is ho-ly ground.

Chorus

Ho-ly ground, I'm stand-ing on ho-ly ground for the

This song is recorded on the Spring Harvest 1998 r:age Album
and on the Spring Harvest 1998 Live Worship Album.

Lord my God is here with me.

136a Morning Prayer

One thing I have asked of the Lord,
this is what I seek:
that I may dwell in the house of the Lord
all the days of my life;
to behold the beauty of the Lord
and to seek Him in His temple.

Call: Who is it that you seek?
Response: **We seek the Lord our God.**

Call: Do you seek Him with all your heart?
Response: **Amen. Lord, have mercy.**

Call: Do you seek Him with all your soul?
Response: **Amen. Lord, have mercy.**

Call: Do you seek Him with all your mind?
Response: **Amen. Lord, have mercy.**

Call: Do you seek Him with all your strength?
Response: **Amen. Christ, have mercy.**

With thanks to the Northumbria Community for permission to use these words from
'A Northumbrian Office'© Northumbria Community Trust, Hetton Hall, Chatton, Alnwick,
Northumberland, NE66 5SD.

137 Time And Again

Caroline Bonnett,
Sue Rinaldi
& Steve Bassett

Gently ♩ = 70

Time and a-gain —— I come back to you
like it was the first time. Time and a-gain —
you re-store my soul like dew —— in the
morn-ing, so gra-cious and kind and slow to

Chorus

This song is recorded on the Spring Harvest 1998 New Songs Album.

137a Prayer Of Humble Access

We do not presume to come to this your table,
merciful Lord, trusting in our own righteousness,
but in your manifold and great mercies.
We are not worthy so much as to
gather up the crumbs under your table.
But you are the same Lord
whose nature is always to have mercy.
Grant us therefore, gracious Lord,
so to eat the flesh of your dear Son Jesus Christ
and to drink his blood,
that we may evermore dwell in him
and he in us. **Amen.**

138   To Be In Your Presence
(My Desire)

Noel Richards
Arr. L. Evans

This song is recorded on the Double Album Celebrating 20 Years Of Spring Harvest.

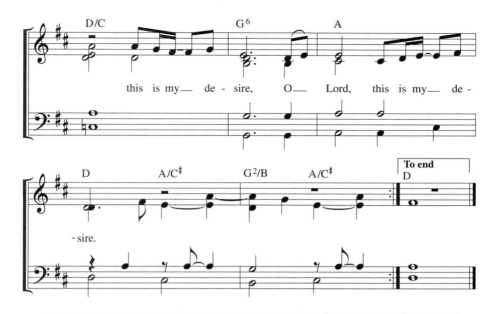

this is my— de - sire, O— Lord, this is my— de -sire.

138a   Evening Office

My soul waits for the Lord
More than those who watch
For the morning.
More than those who
Watch for the morning.

Call: Out of the depths I have cried to you

Response: O Lord, hear my voice

Call: With my whole heart I want to praise You

Response: O Lord, hear my voice

Call: If you, Lord, should mark iniquities

Response: Who could stand? Who could stand?

I will wait for the Lord
My soul waits,
And in His word
Do I hope.

With thanks to the Northumbria Community for permission to use these words from 'A Northumbrian Office' © Northumbria Community Trust, Hetton Hall, Chatton, Alnwick, Northumberland, NE66 5SD.

139 Today I Awake

John L. Bell & Graham Maule

1. To - day I a - wake and God is be - fore me. At night, as I dreamt, he sum - moned the day; for God ne - ver sleeps but pat - terns the morn - ing with
2. To - day I a - rise and Christ is be - side me. He walked through the dark to scat - ter new light. Yes, Christ is a - live, and beck - ons his peo - ple to
3. To - day I af - firm the Spi - rit with - in me at wor - ship and work, in strug - gle and rest. The Spi - rit in - spires all life which is chang - ing from
4. To - day I en - joy the Tri - ni - ty round me, a - bove and be - neath, be - fore and be - hind; the Ma - ker, the Son, the Spi - rit to - geth - er they

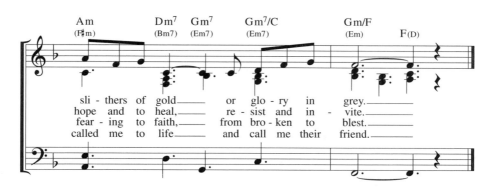

Am (F#m)	Dm7 (Bm7)	Gm7 (Em7)	Gm7/C (Em7)	Gm/F (Em)	F(D)

sli - thers of gold_____ or glo - ry in grey._____
hope and to heal,_____ re - sist and in - vite._____
fear - ing to faith,_____ from bro - ken to blest._____
called me to life_____ and call me their friend._____

139a   A New And Living Way

from Exodus 26

Leader   Let us draw near to God with a sincere heart in full
assurance of faith.

Response   **Because there is a new and living way - through
the curtain - that is Jesus.**

Leader   The Lord said to Moses 'make a curtain of blue, purple
and scarlet linen and this will separate the Holy Place
from the Most Holy Place.'

Blue reflected His origin.

Response   **He came from Heaven.**

Leader   Purple reflected His royalty.

Response   **He was a King.**

Leader   Scarlet reflected His blood.

Response   **Shed for us.**

Leader   This is the new and living way.
Into the Most Holy Place.

Reponse   **He has made us perfect by His blood.**

Somehow, understanding the relevance of the curtain and it's purpose, helps us to grasp the awesome
nature of God, allowing Jesus to die. And the realisation that follows of how **we** can enter that Most
Holy Place, prompts us to want to praise Him more. If there is any way to enable people to actually
see these colours, even better.

140 To You, O Lord

1. To you, O Lord, I lift up my soul,
2. Show me your ways and teach me your paths,
3. Re-mem-ber, Lord, your mer-cy and love

in you I trust, O my God.
guide me in truth, lead me on;
that e-ver flow from of old.

Do not let me be put to shame,
for you're my God, you are my Sa-viour,
Re-mem-ber not the sins of my youth

nor let my e-ne-mies tri-umph o-ver me.
my hope is in you each mo-ment of the day.

141 We Bow Down

Gently, with awe

Viola Grafstrom

We bow down and con - fess You are Lord in this place. We bow down and con - fess You are Lord in this place. You are all I need; it's Your face I seek. In the pre - sence of Your light we bow down, we bow down.

This song is recorded on the Spring Harvest 1998 New Songs Album.

142 We Have Sung Our Songs
(How Long?)

Stuart Townend

Thoughtfully

Verse

1. We have sung our songs of vic-tory, we have prayed to you for rain; we have cried for your com-pas-sion to re-new the land a-gain. Now we're

2. Lord, we know your heart is bro-ken by the e-vil that you see, and you've stayed your hand of judge-ment for you plan to set men free. But the

3. But I know a day is com-ing when the deaf will hear his voice, when the blind will see their Sa-viour, and the lame will leap for joy. When the

143 We Sing Your Mercies

Steadily, with strength

Mark Altrogge

We sing your mer - cies, we sing your end - less prais - es,

we sing your ev - er - last - ing love.

We sing your mer - cies, we sing your end - less prais - es,

Sov - 'reign One who died,

This song is recorded on the Spring Harvest 1999 New Songs Album.

Sov-'reign One who died for us.

(Fine)

Verse

1. Should he who made the stars be hung up-on a tree?
2. Should he who is the Light be cast in-to the dark?

And should the hands that healed be
And should the Lord of love be

driv-en through for me? Should he who gave us bread
pierced through his own heart? Should he who called us friends

be — made to swal - low gall?____ Should
be de - sert - ed by___ us all?____ Should

he who gave___ us breath___ and life___ be
he who lived___ a sin - less life___ be

slaugh - tered for us all?_____
pun - ished for our fall?_____

143a Families And Relationships
James 1: 2-8

Consider it pure joy, my brothers, whenever you face trials of many kinds, because you know that the testing of your faith develops perseverance. Perseverance must finish its work so that you may be mature and complete, not lacking anything. If any of you lacks wisdom, he should ask God, who gives generously to all without finding fault, and it will be given to him. But when he asks, he must believe and not doubt, because he who doubts is like a wave of the sea, blown and tossed by the wind. That man should not think he will receive anything from the Lord; he is a double-minded man, unstable in all he does.

144 We're Looking To Your Promise
(Send Revival)

Matt Redman

Steadily

1. We're look-ing to your pro-mise of old,___ that if we__ pray__
   look-ing to the pro-mise you made,___ that if we__ turn__

___ and hum-ble our - selves,___ you will__ come__
___ and look to your__ face,___ you will__ come

___ and heal our__ land,___ you will come,___
___ and heal our__ land,___ you will come,___

1.

___ you will come.___   2. We're
___ you will come___

357

145 We Will Give Ourselves No Rest
(Knocking On The Door Of Heaven)

With conviction
Capo 3 (D)

Matt Redman
& Steve Cantellow

We will give our-selves— no rest— 'till your king-dom comes— on earth;— you've po-si-tioned watch - men on— the walls.— Now our prayers will flow— like tears,— for you've shared your heart— with us;—

God of hea-ven, on our knees we fall. Come
down in pow-er, re - veal your heart a - gain; come
hear our cries, the tears that plead for rain. We're
knock-ing, knock-ing on the door of hea - ven, we're
watch-ing, watch-ing on the walls to see you, we're
cry - ing, cry - ing for this ge - ne - ra - tion, we're
look-ing, look-ing for a time of break - through, we're

pray - ing for your name to be known
pray - ing for your word to bear fruit

in all of the earth. We're
in all of the

earth, in all of the earth.

145a The Great Commission
Matthew 28: 18-20

Then Jesus came to them and said, "All authority in heaven and earth has been given to me. Therefore go and make disciples of all nations, baptising them in the name of the Father and of the Son and of the Holy Spirit, and teaching them to obey everything I have commanded you. And surely I am with you always, to the very end of the age."

145b   Blessing

May the peace of the Lord Christ go with you,
wherever He may send you,

May He guide you through the wilderness,
protect you through the storm.

May He bring you home rejoicing
at the wonders He has shown you,

May He bring you home rejoicing
once again into our doors.

145c   The Call To Watch And Pray
from Mark 13: 1-37

Leader   Heaven and earth will pass away, but my words will
never pass away.

Response   **This is the call from Jesus.**

Leader   Watch and pray, be on your guard.
Do not be deceived.

Response   **Your words will never pass away.**

Leader   Holy Spirit, help us to watch and pray.
Teach us to hold on to You, not to our lives.
Teach us to listen to Your words, not to our own.
Teach us not to look back, but to wait in obedience.

Response   **Because this is the call of Jesus, this prayer we pray.**
Amen.

A time of silence is kept as an act of waiting.

Based on Mark 13 'The call to watch and pray' reflects Jesus' urgency about the end of the age. The words
watch and *be on your guard* are repeated often in this chapter. And because this is a call from Jesus
himself we should take it very seriously. The prayer is that not only do we stay alert but that wait on Him
as to how we live our lives. the silence is crucial as we have to give God the opportunity to speak.

146 We've Been Crying Out
(Breath Of Heaven, Come)

Andy Smith
& Johnny Markin

Steadily

1. We've been cry-ing out— for mer-cy for— our
   hold-ing out— a can-dle in— the

land: prayers have flowed— with tears to see your heal-ing
night: feed the fra-gile flame to see it burn-ing

hand. To com-fort all the suf-fer-ing— we
bright. To bring your hope to vil-la-ges— and

see, loos-en-ing— the chains, pro-claim-ing li-ber-ty.—
towns, in ev-ery ci-ty street may hea-ven's song re-sound..-

So we're calling out your name unto
Jesus once again, flood this thirsty ground,— see you
turn it all— around. Hear the desperate cries and
open up— their eyes, let them see— your love. Oh, oh
breath of heaven come!   2. We are

147 What A Friend
(Calon Lan)

Last time to Coda ⊕

peace · · · we of-ten for-feit,— oh what
find · · · a friend so faith-ful,— who will
friends · · · mis-un-der-stand you,— take it

need-less · · · pain we bear——— all be-cause—
all——— our sor-rows share: Je-sus knows—
to——— the Lord in prayer. In his arms—

——— we do not car-ry e-ve-ry-thing—
——— our ev-ery weak-ness, take it——— to—
——— he'll take and shield you, you——— will find—

——— to God in prayer.
the Lord in prayer.
some com-fort

147a   Break Down The Walls

Break down the walls I have built
keeping you distant
See through the smile that I wear when we meet
Break through the pride that hides the truth
of my condition
Break down the walls around my heart
Make me real, make me real.

With thanks to the Northumbria Community for permission to use these words by Paul Brain
© Northumbria Community Trust.

148 What A Friend I've Found

♩ = 72

Martin Smith

1. What a friend I've found, clo - ser than a
2. What a hope I've found, more faith - ful than a

bro - ther; I have felt your touch, more in - ti - mate than
mo - ther; it would break my heart to e - ver lose each

lov - ers. Je - sus, Je -
oth - er.

-sus, Je - sus, friend for e - ver.

**This song is recorded on the Spring Harvest 1997 Live Worship Album - Volume 2
and on the Double Album Celebrating 20 Years Of Spring Harvest.**

149 What Love Is This?
(I Surrender)

Simply

Dave Bilbrough

1. What love is this—— that took my place? In-stead of wrath— you poured your grace on me. What can I do—— but sim-ply come and wor - ship you?

that comes to save? Up - on that cross— you bore my guilt and shame. To you a - lone— I give my heart and wor - ship you.

no man has seen; it breaks sin's power— and sets this pris - oner free. With all I have— and all I am I wor - ship you.

I sur - ren - der, I sur-

ren - der, I sur - ren - der all to you. 2. What love is this— 3. A great - er love—

149a Through The Rising Of Your Son

Leader: Almighty God,
through the rising of your Son from the grave,
you broke the power of the grave,
you broke the power of death
and condemned death itself to die.

As we celebrate this great triumph
may we also make it the model for our living.

ALL: HELP US TO IDENTIFY IN OUR LIVES
ALL THAT SHOULD RIGHTLY DIE -
REDUNDANT RELATIONSHIPS,
TIRED HABITS,
FRUITLESS LONGINGS.

RESURRECT IN OUR LIVES
FAITH, HOPE AND LOVE
AS SURELY AS YOU RAISED JESUS CHRIST
FROM THE GRAVE.
AMEN.

150

When I Survey
Traditional

Words: Issac Watts
Music adapted by E. Miller

♩ = 88

1. When I sur - vey the wond - rous cross on which the Prince of Glo - ry died, my rich - est gain I count as loss and pour con - tempt on all my pride.

2. For - bid it, Lord, that I should boast save in the cross of Christ my God: the ve - ry things that charm me most - I sac - ri - fice them to his blood.

3. See from his head, his hands, his feet, sor - row and love flow ming - led down: when did such love and sor - row meet or thorns com - pose so rich a crown.

4. Were the whole realm of na - ture mine, that were an of - fering far too small; love so a - maz - ing, so di - vine, de - mands my soul, my life my all!

370

151 When I Survey
Celtic

Words. Issac Watts
Music. Trad
Arr. Dave Bainbridge, Joanne Hogg
& Teri Bryant

With a slow lilt

1. When I sur-vey the wond-rous cross
2. For-bid it, Lord, that I should boast
3. See from his head, his hands, his feet,
4. Were the whole realm of na-ture mine,

on which the Prince of Glo-ry died,
save in the death of Christ my Lord:
sor-row and love flow ming-led down:
that were an of-fering far too small;

my rich-est gain I count but loss
all the vain things that charm me most
did e'er such love and sor-row meet
love so a-maz-ing, so di-vine,

and pour con-tempt on all my pride.
I sac-ri-fice them to his blood.
or thorns com-pose so rich a crown.
de-mands my soul, my life my all!

152   When The Music Fades
(Heart Of Worship)

1. When the mu - sic fades, ____ all is stripped a - way ___
2. King of end - less worth, ____ no one could ex - press ___

____ and I sim - ply come, ____
____ how much you de - serve. ____

long - ing just to bring ____ some - thing that's of worth.
Though I'm weak and poor, ____ all I have is yours,

____ that will bless your heart. ____
____ ev - ery sin - gle breath. ____

This song is recorded on the Spring Harvest 1998 New Songs Album and the 1998 Praise Mix.

I'll bring you more than a song,—— for a song in it-self
is not what you have re-quired.——
You search much deep-er with-in—— through the way things ap-pear,
you're look-ing in-to my heart.————

153 Who Is There Like You?

With a gentle rhythm
Capo 3 (D)

Paul Oakley

Who is there like you, and who else would give their life for me, even suffering in my place? And who could repay you? All of creation looks to you,

This song is recorded on the Spring Harvest 1999 New Songs Album.

and you— pro-vide—— for all you— have——— made.

Chorus
So I'm lift-ing up my hands, lift-ing up my voice, lift-ing up your

name, and in your grace I——— rest, for your love has come to—

me and— set me free.——— And I'm trust-ing in your

word, trust-ing in your cross, trust-ing in your blood and all your faith-ful -

ness, for your power at work in me is—— chang - ing me.——

153a Everything Happens
from Ecclesiastes 3

Leader: Everything that happens on earth
happens at the time God chooses.

Women: God sets the time for birth and the time for death,
Men: the time for sorrow and the time for joy,

Women: the time for tearing and the time for mending,
Men: the time for scattering and the time for gathering.

Women: the time for seeking and the time for losing,
Men: the time for keeping silence and the time for speaking.

Leader: Everything that happens on earth
ALL: HAPPENS AT THE TIME GOD CHOOSES.

154   Who Sees It All

Graham Kendrick

1. Who sees it all, before whose gaze is dark-est night bright as the day;—
2. Who sees it all, the debt that's owed of lives un-lived of love un-known?—
3. Who knows the fears that drive a choice, un-bur-ies pain and gives it voice?—
4. Whose an-ger burns at what we've done then bears our sin as if his own?—
5. Whose bro-ken heart up-on a cross won free-dom, joy and peace for us?—

watch-ing as in the se-cret place his like-ness forms up-on a face?—
Who weighs the loss of in-no-cence, or feels the pain of our of-fence?—
And who can wash a me-mo-ry, or take the sting of death a-way?—
Who will re-ceive us as we are whose arms are wide and wait-ing now?—
Whose blood re-deems, who ev-er lives and all be-cause of love for-gives?—

155 With All My Heart

Moderately
Capo 2 (D)

Steve McGregor

With all my heart, I will put my trust in you.

1. in you.
2. in you.

I will lean on— you, de-pend on— you,

I will look to— the one I love—

156 With The Choirs Of Angels
Singing *(Hallelujah Song)*

Steadily, building

Matt Redman

1. With the choirs of an - gels sing - ing,
2. With the liv - ing crea - tures speak - ing
3. I would bring this praise like in - cense

and the realm of heav - enly hosts; as those el - ders
praise and praise and praise a - gain; with the com - pa -
ris - ing to your throne a - bove, fill the air with

humb - ly bow, I'd love to come to your throne with a
ny of heaven, I'd love to come to your throne with a
heart filled songs in har - mo - ny and me - lo - dy to the

sim - ple song.___ (Mmm___)
song of love.___
One I love.___

Hal - le - lu - jah, Je - sus, hal - le - lu - jah,

hal - le - lu. Hal - le - lu - jah, Je - sus,

pour - ing out my heart to you.

heart to you. (And) who can tell the a - dor - a - tion

that will rise up to your throne? Ev-ery knee that

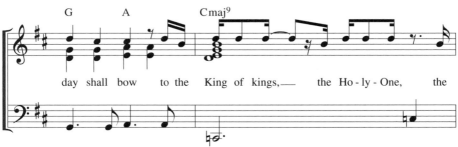

day shall bow to the King of kings,— the Ho-ly - One, the

on - ly One.— We'll all be sing-ing... Hal - le - lu - jah.

156a A Prayer Of Self-Offering
from Mark 14: 1-10

During a time of quiet worship this prayer could be read by the leader with time
between each line for individuals to respond.

You are perfect and precious Lord Jesus.
Yet I have no precious perfume to offer You.
Only my need.
My shame.
My brokeness.
My longings.
My self.
Can this be beautiful to You?
Perfect, precious Jesus.
This is my offering.

Bridges — From G

To B♭

To C

To D

To E♭

To F

157 You Are A Kind And Loving God
(You Care For Us)

Judy Bailey

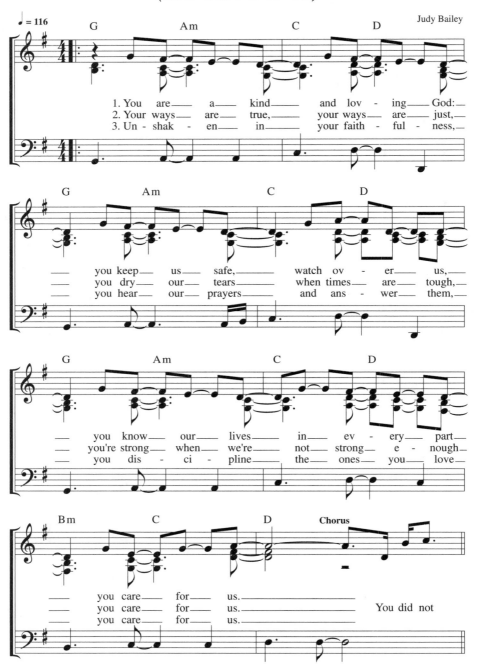

1. You are a kind and lov-ing God:
   you keep us safe, watch ov-er us,
   you know our lives in ev-ery part
   you care for us.

2. Your ways are true, your ways are just,
   you dry our tears when times are tough,
   you're strong when we're not strong e-nough
   you care for us. You did not

3. Un-shak-en in your faith-ful-ness,
   you hear our prayers and ans-wer them,
   you dis-ci-pline the ones you love
   you care for us.

This song is recorded on the Spring Harvest 1998 Praise Mix.

158 You Are Holy

Reuben Morgan

This song is recorded on the Spring Harvest 1999 New Songs Album.

159 You Are Merciful To Me

Ian White

159a Celtic Night Prayer (2)

Deliver us, Lord, from every evil
And grant us peace in our day.
In mercy, Lord, keep us free from sin,
And protect us from all anxiety
as we wait in joyful hope
For the coming of our saviour, Jesus Christ.
Let your Kingdom come, Lord, in me.

160 You Are The One I Come To Worship (*Only You*)

Steadily

Simon Parkin

1. You are the one I come to wor -
   I bow to al -
   of all my hea -
   er of my heart's

- ship, pour out my life in - to your pre -
- ways, hop - ing to catch one glimpse of glo -
- ven, I sing with the an - gels of your great -
- gold, hold - ing the plans of all the un -

- sence, pray - ing your eyes of love would
- ry; long - ing to touch the cloak of
- ness: you are the on - ly one to
- told; and still the King of kings would

1.,3.

fall up-on__ this soul.
call this soul__ their own. 2. You are the Lord__
4. You are the keep__

2.,4.

grace that sets__ me free.__
call this fool__ his friend.__ On-ly

you (on-ly you) on-ly you (on-ly you) on-ly you (on-ly you)

(Fine)

Je-sus.__ On-ly you (on-ly you) my King. 3. You are the king__

393

161 You Make Your Face
(And That My Soul Knows Very Well)

Moderately

Darlene Zschech
& Russell Fragar

1. You make your face to shine on me, and that my
2. Joy and strength each day I'll find, and that my

soul knows ve-ry well; you lift me up, I'm
soul knows ve-ry well; for-give-ness, hope I

cleansed and free, and that my soul knows ve-ry well.
know is mine, and that my soul knows ve-ry well.

Chorus

— When moun-tains fall I'll stand by the pow-

This song is recorded on the Spring Harvest 1999 Praise Mix.

er of— your hand,— and in your heart— of hearts— I'll dwell,—

_____ and that my soul— knows ve-ry well.—

When moun-tains fall— —

161a Christ, Proclaimed
from 1 Timothy 3 & 2 Timothy 2

Let us declare our faith

**We believe in one Lord, Jesus Christ
he was revealed in the flesh,
attested by the Spirit, seen by angels,
proclaimed among the nations,
believed in throughout the world, and taken up to glory.**

If we died with him, **we shall live with him.**
If we endure, **we shall reign with him. Amen.**

162 You Have Given Me New Life *(Over Me)*

Nathan & David Fellingham

1. You have giv - en me new life;
   now my heart is sa - tis - fied.
   I'm tast - ing the pow - er of the age to come,

2. I've ne - ver had a friend like you;
   all that you've pro - mised you will do.
   I'm drink - ing from the foun - tain that will ne - ver run dry,

I'm liv-ing in___ the glo-ry of___ the
I'm liv-ing in___ the joy___ of___ a

re - sur - rect - ed Son.___ I'm walk-ing in___ the light___
heart that's pu - ri-fied.___ I'm walk-ing now___ with you,___

and all that I___ now do___ is___ for you.
and all I have___ is yours,___ take___ my life.

Chorus

Pour-ing o - ver me,_____ ev-er-last - ing love_____ and mer-cy,
Pour-ing o - ver me,_____ a - bound - ing grace_____ so free,_____

o - ver me in a flood_____ of pow'r._____
o - ver me your un -

2.

end - - - - - ing love._____

Last time

end - - - - - ing love._____

163 You're The Lion Of Judah
(Lion Of Judah)

1. You're the Lion of Judah, the Lamb that was slain, you ascended to heaven and evermore will reign; at the end of the age when the earth you reclaim, you will gather the nations be-

2. There's a shield in our hand and a sword at our side, there's a fire in our spirit that cannot be denied; as the Father has told us, for these you have died, for the nations that gather be-

who was slain for the world — rule in power.'

And the earth will re - ply: 'You shall reign

as the King of all kings and the Lord of all lords.'

401

164 Your Name Is Great

Trish Morgan

Majestically

Your name is great, _____ your name is
strong, _____ your name is
chains, _____ your power is

good, _____ your name brings life _____ like no oth - er
true, _____ Lord, no - one else _____ can love like
shown, _____ ov - er fo - reign skies _____ your name is

could. _____ Your name is high _____ through - out the
you. _____ Your name can save, _____ the wa - ters
known. _____ Your name brings light, _____ the de - mons

earth, with ev - ery breath we'll sing your
part, your name can heal the bro - ken _____
flee, your name will last e - ter - nal -

165 Yours Is The Kingdom
(Hopes And Dreams)

Paul Field

Yours is the king-dom of hopes and dreams, yours is the pow-er of love; yours is the glo-ry of heaven on earth for ev - er and ev - er, for ev - er a - men.

1. God of the
2. God of the

fu - ture, God of the past; God of the here and
bo - dy, God of the soul; God of the heart and

now we come be - fore you to a - dore
mind: you stand be - side us, you will guide

you, ev - ery knee shall bow.
us God of our time.

165a Into A Desert Place

Lord,
let our memory provide no shelter for grievance against another.
Lord,
let our heart provide no harbour for hatred of another.
Lord,
let our tongue be no accomplice in the judgement of a sister or a
brother.

With thanks to the Northumbrian Community for permission to use these words from 'A Northumbrian Office' © Northumbria Community Trust, Hetton Hall, Chatton, Alnwick, Northumberland, NE66 5SD.

Guitar Chords

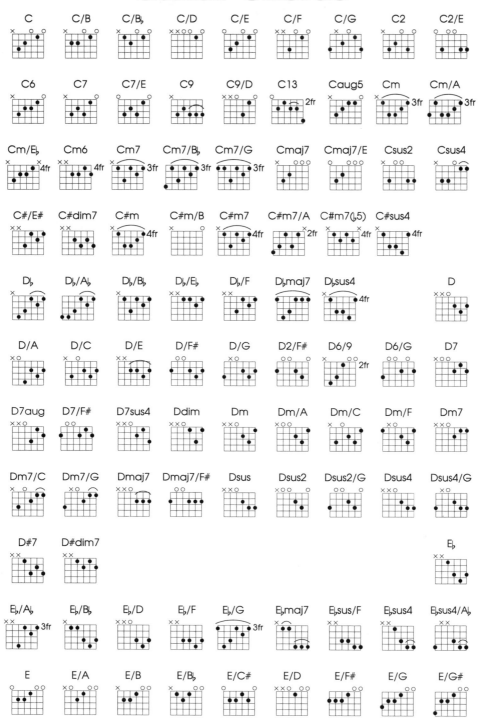

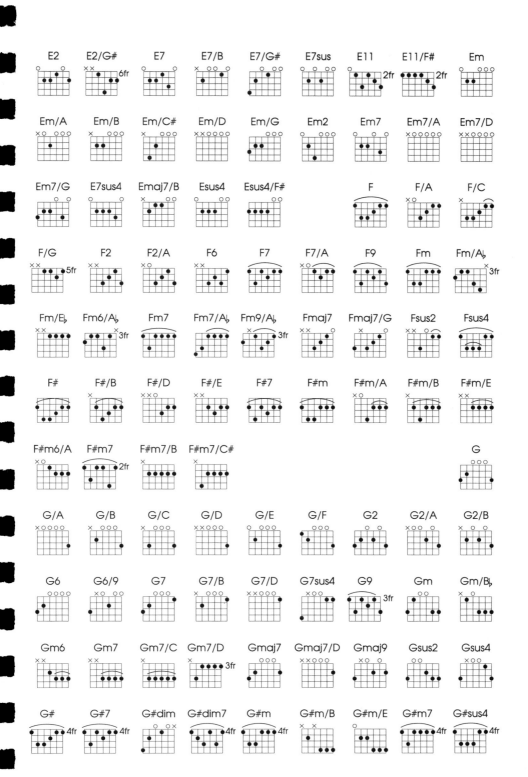

Guitar Chords — continued

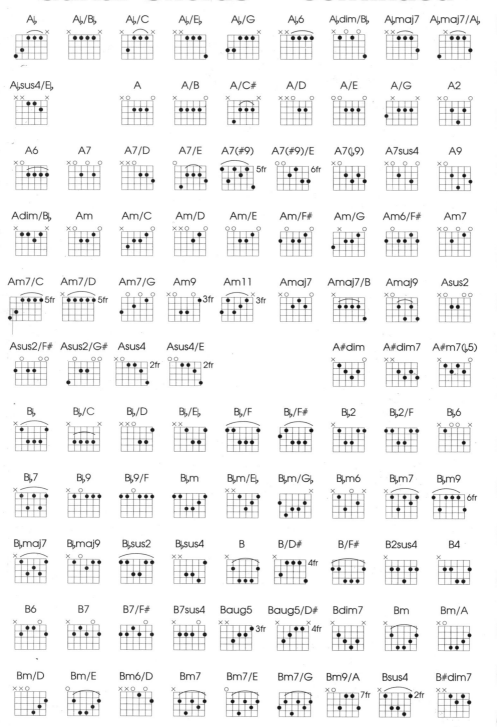